mountain animals

D0419813

Tony Long

mountain animals

A Macdonald Pictureback **Animal Life Series**

The author of
Mountain animals
Tony Long

Series editor
**Cathy Jarman
BSc FZS**

Zoological consultant
Dr Malcolm Coe

Tony Long is a young
naturalist in his early
twenties. For two years he
worked on the successful
'Purnell's encyclopedia of
animal life'. Extremely
interested in the conservation
of endangered animal species
he is spending 1972 studying
the markhor, a rare wild
goat, in part of its range in
the rugged mountains of the
western Himalayas.

Author of 'Evolution of
life', 'Animals of Europe'
and 'Migration of Birds and
Animals', Cathy Jarman was
executive editor of 'Purnell's
encyclopedia of animal life'.
Previously a lecturer at the
Zoological Society of London
to children and students, she
has travelled to Australia,
Japan and South Africa to
observe and study animals in
their natural surroundings.

Dr Malcolm Coe is a lecturer
in animal ecology at the
University of Oxford.
Previous to this he lectured
in zoology at the University
College of Nairobi while also
carrying out research on
Mount Kenya's ecology. At
present he is co-ordinating
research on giant tortoises.
He is author of 'The Ecology
in the Alpine Zone of Mount
Kenya'.

Publisher   **John Thompson**

Editorial   **Carolyn Barber,
Alison Maddock, Christine McMullen**

Picture Editor   **Jackie Sober**

Design Controller   **Don Mason**

Designer   **Graham Marshall**

Production   **Thelma Rolfe**

Special drawings   **Tudor Art**

Copyright © 1971:
Macdonald

First published by
Macdonald
St Giles House
49 Poland Street
London W1

Made and printed
in Great Britain by
Hazell Watson and
Viney Ltd.

Contents

Editor's note

This book is a popular account of animals living in the mountains of the world. Mountains come in all different shapes and sizes and climatic conditions vary enormously. The animals which inhabit the mountain tops also come in a wide range of size and shape, many with special adaptations to fit a certain niche in the mountain environment. The rocky mountain goat, for example, is the most sure footed of all mountain creatures. It can move along ledges which are so narrow they appear impassable. Cold does not bother this animal either; it has a short woolly undercoat and a thick shaggy outer coat. The mountain goat combats the rocky heights while the dipper, a small waterbird, struggles successfully against swift, freezing cold streams where it forages for aquatic insect larvae and beetles, even though the temperature of the air is well below zero.

The author enquires into the lives of these and many other mountain animals, including llama, cougar, grizzly, pika, golden eagle, snow leopard and even the abominable snowman, the yeti. He explains in simple terms how these high-living creatures come to terms with the surrounding conditions.

Tony Long also surveys man at high altitudes, from the peoples of the Himalayas and the Andes to the men who have felt the urge to climb mountains.

Attic of the world

Mountains are the beginning and the end of all natural scenery.

John Ruskin. 'Modern Painters'. Vol 4, Pt V, Chap 20

Relics of the earth's stormy past, the great mountain ranges of the world form a treasure-house of unique and rare forms of life. Only those animals which are able to adapt to the piercing cold and lack of oxygen can survive on the heights, but the lower, sunnier slopes offer a great variety of desirable habitats.

Each autumn, almost unnoticed over the vast Himalayan mountain range, greylag geese make one of the world's hardest journeys. Nearly five miles above the level of the sea, thousands of these birds in great 'V' formations head away from the oncoming bitterness of the Siberian winter, towards the warmth of Bengal. The geese fly over the high peaks, and although they tolerate the icy, airless wastes of great altitude, they are 'just passing through'. A few thousand feet below are creatures which live permanently in the inhospitable mountains. They come from all sections of the animal kingdom. There are tiny fleas in the ice cracks of the glaciers. The snow partridge nests nearly up to the snowline, and the accentor, a relative of the hedge sparrow, goes higher. Sheep and goats push away snow to feed on the sparse plants beneath, and gnawing creatures tunnel through the snow for protection and food.

Animals have found many ways to live in the harshness of the heights. Man has been more inhibited. Only in the last few thousand years has he colonized the highlands. Superstition has had much to do with this. It is not difficult to understand the attitudes of the monks of Japan who still regard the mighty, snow-capped volcano Fujiyama as sacred, and of the tribesmen around cloud-shrouded Mount Kenya who believe their gods live there. As technology expands, however, changes come. Money, in the shape of ores and minerals, and challenge, in attempts to climb summits, draw more and more people to them. As always, the naturalist follows close on the heels of any kind of explorer. The mountains have given him much that is unique, but this is not the most fascinating study. Interest centres round the way in which familiar

Mountains and highlands

1. *Brooks range*
2. *Alaska range*
3. *Rockies*
4. *Sierra Madre*
5. *Appalachians*
6. *Andes*
7. *Scandinavian Highlands*
8. *Scottish Highlands*
9. *Pyrenees*
10. *Alps*
11. *Carpathians*
12. *Atlas mountains*
13. *Ethiopian plateau*
14. *Ruwenzori*
15. *East African Highlands*
16. *Drakensburg*
17. *Urals*
18. *Caucasus*
19. *Tibetan plateau*
20. *Himalayas*
21. *Kolyma mountains*
22. *Great Dividing Range*

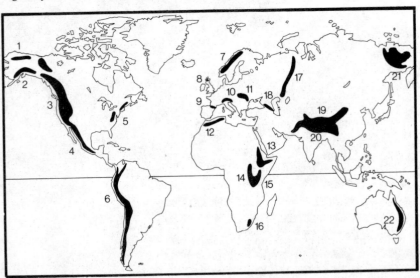

animal types have adapted to one of nature's most inhospitable homes and their reasons for doing so. Earth's history, too, is bound up in the very rocks that form the highlands.

For centuries men have pondered upon stone images of sea shells found miles from the sea and high above its level. It is now known that the weakness of the ancient sea beds put them there. Earth's solid outer crust is not thick, and its most fragile areas are the beds of seas. Here the rock is made of countless shells, cases, and the hard remains of creatures which have sunk to the sea-bed for millions of years. A few short miles below the crust lie the forces that build mountains. Immense currents of semi-liquid rock create appropriately powerful stresses at the surface. Over thousands of millions of years it yields under the strain, folding, rippling and buckling at its weaker points. Thus were born most of our modern mountains. The Alps, the Rockies, the Carpathians, the Pyrenees, the Caucasus, the Himalayas – all rose in this fashion, and are said to be sedimentary in origin. The peak of Everest, earth's highest point, is made of marine sandstone.

Folded mountains, as described, are slow to rise and slower to wear away. While it is interesting to compare the worn, low, and aged Welsh and Scots mountains with the tall, jagged and young Himalayas, there is a far more entertaining and spectacular way in which mountains can rise – and be lost. This is the volcano, a peak formed by the release of molten rock through a crack in the crust. Some of the greatest peaks are volcanic; Mount Kenya and Kilimanjaro in East Africa and Mount Ararat in Eastern Turkey are examples. Some idea of the forces stored within volcanoes can be taken from the partial disappearance of the island of Krakatoa, a volcanic peak, in August 1833. One of its eruptions took the form of an explosion which was heard 3,000 miles away, and which threw some five cubic miles of material into the atmosphere. Two-thirds of the island disappeared. Not all volcanic risings, however, result from eruptions. Sometimes great domes of rock are pushed up from below, and liquid never reaches the surface. The Henry mountains of Utah are an example.

Volcanoes take their toll of men. Over 30,000 people perished in the great waves of water thrown up by Krakatoa, and the eruption of Vesuvius buried the whole of Pompeii in 79 A.D. The earthquake, a by-product of the last method of mountain-building, has also caused its share of human suffering. Great blocks of the earth crack and slip in what is known technically as a fault, and the higher block often projects above the surface. Although nothing on such a massive scale has happened in man's recorded history, there is a fault separating the Scottish Highlands and the Midland

Sculptures of the heights

1. *The slopes of tropical Mount Kenya are richly covered with the giant tree groundsel, a unique East African mountain species which grows up to 20 feet.*

2. *Spectacular peaks have been formed by the weathering of limestone in the Dolomites, a range situated in Italy just south of the Austrian Tyrol.*

3. *Stark and isolated, Mount Suilven – meaning pillar – raises its sandstone cliffs steeply from the low, undulating plains of northwest Scotland.*

4. *The jagged saw-tooth profile of peaks in the Colorado Rockies contrast strongly with the smooth, glacier-scoured valley, now filled by a lake.*

5. *Above the cloud the snowy slopes of Mount Kilimanjaro catch the sun. Its flat top is the crater edge of an extinct volcano. Below, impala buck graze the Kenyan plateau.*

4

Valley which measures 10,000 feet from the bottom of the crack, deep in the earth, to the top, which projects only two or three thousand feet above the surface. It is known as the Highland Boundary Fault, and it runs from the mouth of the Clyde on the west coast to Stonehaven on the east.

Life at low pressure

No two mountain ranges are alike. Each has its own characteristics, shown not only by its animal life but by its influence on the surrounding climate and distribution of the animals. The greatest of the mountain masses is the Himalayas, running approximately east-west and forming a barrier between the Asiatic tropics and the temperate zone. As such the range extends, with outlying ranges, eastwards into China and westwards to the mountains of Iran and the Near East, giving it a north-south mixture of animals.

The peaks of Africa and Australia are more island-like. The high mountains of Ethiopia and central and South Africa form isolated patches, known as terrestrial islands, with no barrier formation or common links. Much the same situation exists in Australia and New Zealand. It is in America that the mountains, because of their position, affect the geography of the animals found there. The Rockies extend north-south from Alaska to Central America, then, after a short break in the isthmus of Panama, continue as the Andes to form a western border for South America. They are a barrier between animals of the lowlands of east and west but for mountain dwellers they offer a route to new grounds. The American mountains form a highway along which animals of the north, such as the mountain lion, caribou, and several game birds, can extend their range, still in cold country, down to the tropics.

For all the individual differences between mountains

Dome mountains are formed when igneous rocks, such as granite, are forced upwards under pressure into the upper layers of the earth's crust. Weathering processes denude the surface of softer rock layers and the dome mountain is left exposed.

Fold mountains occur when the surface strata is compressed. The buckles and complex folds that result form ranges such as the Alps but the effects of weathering and further earth movements often alter the fold mountain's appearance.

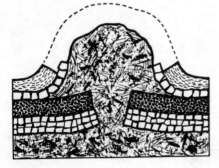

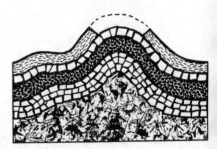

Left. *The 1968 Olympics, held in Mexico City at 7,400 feet, took their toll of the long distance competitors because of the lack of oxygen. This British athlete, Herriott, collapsed at the end of the 3,000 metre steeplechase.*

all high places present similar problems of temperature and pressure to their inhabitants. Air pressure drops with increasing altitude – a situation driven home to sportsmen by the 1968 Olympic Games, held at 7,400 feet in Mexico City. Controversy about acclimatization and the stress factors of thinner air still rages. The facts, however, remain; times in sprint events were faster (less air resistance) and the long distance events suffered (lack of oxygen). The highest permanent human settlement is at about 16,000 feet in Tibet, though herdsmen and their animals go up to 2,000 feet higher. Wild sheep and ibex range up to 19,000 feet in Tibet, with wolves and foxes a little lower and yaks managing even higher. These figures are amazing when one considers that oxygen pressure at 18,000 feet is half that at sea level.

Many birds are presented with flying difficulties in thin air. Some species, however, have mastered it. Apart from migrating geese and possibly swifts, choughs hold the record for altitude among the larger birds. One chough was seen to take off, with difficulty and a long run-up, from 27,000 feet on the slopes of Everest. The Andean condor, largest of living birds, regularly soars among the

Volcanic activity can build spectacular mountains of lava, cinder and ash. When a volcano cools lava solidifies within the central vent to form a hard plug which may remain long after the volcano cone itself has worn away.

Fault block mountains form along huge cracks in the earth surface. Movements along the plane of the faults cause great rock masses to uplift or slip. These form mountains and areas of high plateaux or sometimes huge rift valleys.

highest South American peaks. Eagles and vultures also seem to have little difficulty in mastering altitude.

Cold-blooded animals are less susceptible to low pressure than are warm-blooded ones. Laboratory experiments on frogs have proved their ability to survive at pressures well below those represented by the highest mountains. Frogs and toads are found at altitude on most of the world's ranges. Insects, too, are able to stand sudden and large drops in pressure. Immature spiders have been found at 22,000 feet in the Himalayas, and only slightly lower down, a tiny community of fleas, springtails and spiders thrives. With no acclimatization, a cricket has been subjected to pressures lower than those at the top of Everest (over 29,000 feet) having been at ground level pressure two minutes previously. Apart from startled twitches when pressure was restored in a rush, the cricket seemed little disturbed. More experiments with different animals have shown that many are surprisingly resistant to pressure change. It is temperature which limits the extent to which the high parts of the world can be colonized.

Cold dictates shape

The temperature of the air drops fairly regularly with height above sea level. The world average is a drop of about 1·7°C for every thousand feet above sea level. The mountains in the tropics have a slower decrease than the mountains of the cooler temperate regions such as the Alps where there is a sharp fall of temperature with increased height. Even on the Equator, however, there is a nightly frost above 11,000 feet. The changes in temperature are directly comparable to those encountered moving from tropics to poles. The vegetation changes on the way up just as it does in the climatic zones of the world. This is particularly well-marked in North America, where grasslands, deserts, or deciduous forests of the lowlands give way on the mountain slopes to taiga-like

Top. *Hamilton's frog is one of three primitive species of frog which now exist only near the tops of mountains in New Zealand, where the air is cool and moist.*

Above. *Many birds of prey are as at home up mountains as on the plains. The African augur buzzard occurs from low country to high forested mountains; on Mount Kenya it can be seen hunting rodents almost up to the snow line.*

Right. *Out-stared by a pair of young Tengmalm's owls. This species ranges over European mountain forests from the Alps and Jura to Scandinavia.*

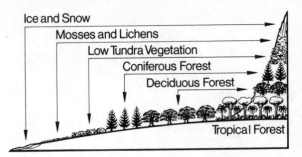

Ice and Snow

Mosses and Lichens

Low Tundra Vegetation

Coniferous Forest

Deciduous Forest

Tropical Forest

Vegetation zones
The sequence of vegetation types from the tropics to the poles (right to left in the diagram) *is often followed by changes seen at successively higher levels up a mountain. This idealized picture is subject to local variation, however. The view in Swedish Lapland* (below) *shows birch woodland giving way to slopes with tundra vegetation and then to bare rocks and snow.*

forests of conifers, and these precede open tundra-like conditions. Since these mountains extend south from the Arctic, many northern animals have made their way along this 'habitat corridor' finding appropriate conditions at ever higher elevations. Thus, like the poles, the highest parts of mountains extend little hospitality; the pressure is low, the temperature often verges on the prohibitive.

As the vegetation on the slopes of mountains parallels that of climatic zones, so the adaptations of the animals are the same. The animals' extremities become smaller as the habitat becomes colder. Mice reared at about 20°C have shorter ears and tails than those from the same stock reared at higher temperatures. This tendency has given rise to some confusion in the naming of mountain species. There was considerable controversy at one time about the separation of chinchillas into mountain and lowland species, mainly on the basis of the length of their tails. It is now agreed that the difference is due to the effect of the cold heights. Animals in cold climates carry their young for longer than their lowland contemporaries; such a long gestation has the advantage that the young are born at a greater stage of development.

Once above the snow line familiar polar adaptations show themselves. Although it is usual for mammals of the colder regions to have small ears, tails and feet, some of them need large ears, tails or feet to survive successfully. So that heat is not lost too quickly to the outside through these enlarged extremities these parts of the body are covered in thick fur to insulate them. There are several examples; comparison between the pads of mountain hares or snow leopards and those of their lowland counterparts verges on the comic. The footpads of the mountain animals are much bigger, so a larger surface area is presented to the snow, thus spreading the weight. The tail of the snow leopard is longer than the head and body. It acts as a counterpoise for the body as the cat needs careful balance when climbing trees, springing on prey or moving over steep slopes. It is useful only at a reasonable length, so it is covered with thick fur to prevent heat loss.

Elevated sanctuary

In the never-ending struggle for space in which to feed, shelter and reproduce, animals of every kind have resorted to inhospitable homes. The Pygmies of the near-impenetrable Ituri jungle; the Bushmen of the searing Kalahari desert; the Ainu, aborigines of Japan who took to the mountains; all these are examples in human communities. These are all very recent and there has been little time for adaptation. In contrast, some animals show remarkable specialization of form.

Fishes of several freshwater families have made their homes in mountain streams – not the tinkling trickles of popular imagination, but the powerful and cold torrents which, in some places, carry boulders along their course as if they were pebbles. Grouped under the general name of hillstream fishes, the occupants of these waterways are perfectly adapted for life around the gullies, potholes and large boulders. Most of them have flattened bodies, and some are almost leaf-like. This shape enables them to allow the water to flow by with a minimum of resistance or drag. Many have lost their scales, which create drag. A striking example of this is the catfish *Astroblepus* of the Andes. Its closest relatives are the armoured catfishes, which derive their name from their coat of heavy scales. *Astroblepus* has a naked skin. All hillstream fishes have some means of clinging to the bottom. Some of the

Rarest and most beautiful of the big cats, the snow leopard is a nocturnal prowler in the highlands of central Asia.

17

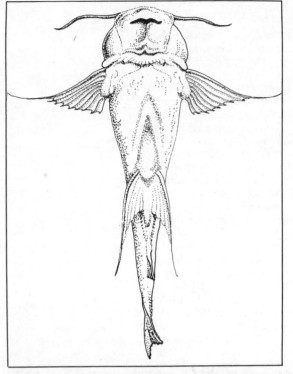

Life in the torrents

Hillstream fish is the group name given to several species in the catfish, loach and carp families, which are especially adapted for life in very fast-flowing mountain streams. Most have some means by which they can cling to a solid support so that they are not dislodged by the current. The naked Andean catfish Astroblepus *(underside shown at left) has a sucker-like mouth for this purpose and a strong muscular tail which helps to control movement in the swift torrent. These two adaptations are used alternately with the gripping action of the pelvic fins when the fish climbs the steep side of a pothole in the river bed, a feat for which this species is renowned. Another sucker-mouthed catfish is shown below in typical bottom-hugging pose.*

Opposite; top. *A herd of caribou find relief from the persistent biting flies of the North American August by resting on an elevated patch of snow.*
Bottom. *High in the Andes, a vicuna grazes amid the ruins of Inca civilization. The vicunas have suffered from intense exploitation. Their fur is the most expensive in the world, and they were in danger of extinction by hunters before many countries banned the import and export of their skins. Poachers, however, still take a large number for the coveted pelt.*
Overleaf. *Casual glance from the mobile eye of a two-lined chameleon. Only in the tropical mountains can reptiles reach great heights. This one lives on Mount Elgon in Kenya, sometimes at heights over 9,000 feet.*

Asiatic catfishes have puckered chests to prevent slipping; in hillstream carps the outer edges of the fins are thickened to form pads, and many have suckers on the chest.

The camel family provides a fine example of survival through adaptation to inaccessible homes. The desert species which have survived on their ability to endure the rigours of desert life are familiar. The only other representatives live in the mountains of South America and, like the camels, have been domesticated to quite a

An elegant mother vicuna and her foal. In the wild this relative of the domesticated llama is confined to the South American highlands at heights of 12 to 16 thousand feet.

large extent. They are the vicuna, guanaco, alpaca and llama.

The ancestors of all these camel-types were widespread in the lowlands of the world about a million years ago. With increasing persecution by predators and competition from other grazing animals, they eventually died out in all but those parts of their range in which their structure gave them an advantage. The llamas' advantage was in the chemical structure of the blood. It has now developed a very high oxygen absorption capacity, and the red blood cells – the transporters of oxygen – have a very long life. The vicuna and the guanaco both exist in the wild – the other two are entirely domestic. The guanacos range from sea level at the southern tip of Patagonia to the highest grasslands of the Andes, but wild vicunas are found only in the mountains between twelve and sixteen thousand feet.

Mountain sanctuary is not all on such a long-term basis. Many animals, particularly predators, suffer in the face of advancing civilization. Cultivation has removed habitats from the lowlands, and some animals have been driven to the slopes where farming is nearly impossible and the timber not good enough to cut. Thus in the eastern United States, the Appalachians and the Adirondacks form a refuge for many animals, like the black bear and the fisher, a type of marten. Both once ranged widely in deciduous forest. The Scandinavian mountains have similarly provided refuge for animals like the wolverine, and the Apennines and the Alps for the ibex.

The protection is not always adequate; man simply will not tolerate large carnivores. The lions disappeared from Europe in the first century A.D., but they persisted in the mountains of North Africa until the 1920s, when the last ones were shot in the Atlas range. Grizzly bears, too, have been exterminated over a very large proportion of their former ranges, and are now found almost exclusively in highlands and the more inaccessible forests. Man's lust for profit has also had its effect. The chinchilla once ranged from sea level to 20,000 feet in the Andes in Peru, Bolivia, Chile and the Argentine. It now survives only at high altitude in the mountains of northern Chile. Even this population would have fallen to the hunters if successful captive breeding had not lowered the price of chinchilla pelts.

Crises of survival like this are becoming increasingly common as man's population and technology expand. The mountains of the world are among the few places left where one can see nature in something approximating to its original balance. Conservationists would do well to turn more attention to them; economically they offer little scope for exploitation and they contain cross-sections of the world's wildlife unequalled in any other habitat.

Smaller ears mean less surface area from which to lose heat, and so it is found that there is a gradation of ear size in relation to body size in hares and rabbits from large in warm climates to small in cold.

Arizona jack rabbit

Oregon jack rabbit

Varying hare

Arctic hare

The maestros

The Chamois inhabits
Lucerne, where his habits
(Though why I have not an idea-r)
Give him sudden short spasms
On the brink of deep chasms,
And he lives in perpetual fear.

'The Chamois' by Hilaire Belloc

Scratching a living on the bleak mountain
slopes at high altitude is no easy matter, but it
is a life for which the agile mountain sheep and
goats are ideally suited. Their breathtaking
leaps and legendary surefootedness on the
crags combine to make them the undisputed
masters of the alpine scene.

Agility is the watchword of the mountain goats, sheep and antelopes. Those people lucky enough to catch a glimpse of these elusive creatures see a display of the most cliff-hanging, apparently suicidal daring as they bound from crag to crag and gallop across apparently vertical cliff faces. This ability, together with their shyness, has made many of them sporting quarry for the rifleman. Yet, even faced with sophisticated firearms, their numbers have suffered only locally. All exaggerated forms of the domestic goat, these animals have spread throughout the mountains of the world, and have such exotic-sounding names as markhor, tahr, and ibex. Because they vary so much in range, shape and horn structure, they are thought to share a long-extinct ancestor. Fossil evidence, although scanty, supports this idea.

Goats and sheep are included in the mammalian group Artiodactyla, which means even-toed. Deer, pigs and giraffes are other animals in this group. Whereas man has five digits (fingers and toes) these animals have only two, the third and fourth digits being extended to form the hoof. The hoof is a very important part of the anatomy of these mountain forms. In types such as the European chamois, the hooves can get a firm grip even on bare rock and the chamois has been described as being shod with horn that wears better than the finest mountain boot. Cup-shaped depressions on the soles of the hooves give a suction-like grip on slippery rocks, and the points of the hoof, the 'aft-claws', grip the surface and help prevent sliding on any but the most icy slopes.

Artiodactyls are herbivores; they eat a variety of plant food. Mountain species exist on a diet of grass, moss and leaves – vegetable matter that contains little nutriment, so they must search constantly for food. They can exist on seemingly bare slopes, rooting out tussocks of grass that grow between rock crevices. The teeth of all herbivores are modified for grinding. The flat teeth called molars are well developed, with projections or cusps forming long ridges. In association with the teeth and food, muscles have developed to work the jaws, giving the characteristic rotary movement seen when the animals are feeding. The tongue is large, extremely long, and has a large number of horny pimples covering its surface that play an important part in cropping and mashing the food. The stomachs of goats and sheep are divided into four chambers, plant food being broken down by contractions of the muscular walls and also by minute organisms that live in the gut (or alimentary tract).

Another adaptation of these mountain-dwelling animals is a co-ordinated system of muscles, tendons and bones that allow them to jump and bound up mountain slopes without any apparent damage. Like other animals living in cold climates, mountain forms usually have

A comparison of the hoof of a chamois, adapted for keeping a foothold on slippery rocks, with those of the klipspringer, which is able to land with all four feet together on a rock, the gerenuk (a browser), and two large-hoofed antelopes which are adapted for ease of movement on soft ground.

chamois

klipspringer

sitatunga

sassaby

gerenuk

thick shaggy coats. As an added protection this is often underlain with denser, fine fur that forms an effective insulating layer against the cold.

Apart from anatomical adaptations, many types behave in a way that ensures survival during harsh conditions, especially during the winter months when food is scarce. The change in feeding habits of the bighorn sheep from autumn through winter has been well recorded. They live for up to half the year in the snowy alpine world of the Canadian Rockies. After the first snowfall of autumn, the sheep crop the tops of grasses that project above the snow. No attempt is made to scrape away snow to reach the more plentiful food beneath. The bighorn has learnt to save its energy for the more rigorous conditions of winter. By selecting the upper part of the plant, containing the seed heads, they obtain the maximum food value for their labours.

After the first heavy snowfall, the sheep begin to push the snow away with their muzzles, but as it starts to pile up they must resort to digging. This activity usually follows a regular pattern. A bighorn will face upslope and dig with his front legs; each stroke is directed to the rear, at a slight angle away from the body. In this way the bighorn can augment the force of each stroke with the force of gravity to dislodge the snow. By mid-winter when conditions become severe, the rams herd together and behave with a 'community spirit'. Lines of rams dig

Bighorn are the agile mountain sheep of the Canadian Rockies, where they live in dry upland country and on mountains above the tree line.

The bighorn year

1. *Shaggy and uncomfortable, bighorn sheep during the moult appear to be diseased as the wool hangs off their backs.*

2. *The breeding season is a time of great rivalry as rams engage in sparring matches, meeting head on and clashing with their horns.*

3. *Although the males fight each other, they do not defend harems of females, and ewes will mate with any male.*

4. *Life in the Rockies is harsh, and food is not easy to find. In autumn the sheep may scratch in the snow or simply graze the tops of the grasses.*

5. *It is in winter that the community spirit shows itself, as groups of rams share the task of digging a trench in the snow to uncover food.*

together on the mountain slopes to form feeding trenches. Feeding and working together in such tight quarters calls for close co-operation. This is unusual in animals that at other times of the year are very hostile towards each other. The feeding lines are made up of males of the same rank, this being measured in bighorn terms by the size of the horns.

Any attempts by younger members to enter the trench are quickly rebuffed. These rejected individuals are thus forced to feed on the more exposed cliffs which, although they support a more scanty vegetation, seem adequate for the needs of juveniles. To conserve energy bighorn feed only during the warmest part of the day and keep well away from the valleys where cold air collects. A weather condition that must be welcomed by the bighorn is the phenomenon called the Chinook. This is a warm, gusty wind that occasionally blows in winter, raising the temperature of the mountain slopes. The consequent thaw brings the bighorn to feed on the exposed grass.

Prince and king of goats

Ibex are probably the best known of the mountain goats. They are distinguished-looking animals with large, scimitar-shaped horns which vary in thickness and proportions in the different types. The name ibex, however, is applied to several types of mountain goat of the genus *Capra*. It is not certain whether these forms are all closely related or whether some of them are derived independently from the true wild goat, or bezoar.

The behaviour of many of the ibex is little known, but thanks to the work of Russian zoologists the habits of the Siberian ibex are now fully recorded. This animal lives between 1,700 and 17,000 feet in the arid mountains of the Russia/Afghanistan border. Herds consist of from three to thirty individuals, but as many as two hundred have been seen feeding together in winter. At this time of year the ibex move down the mountains onto gentle southern slopes. This often takes them down to the forest zone where they feed mainly on leaves. The reproductive behaviour, like that of most mountain goats, is a dramatic affair. The rut, the period of sexual excitement of the males, takes place in the autumn when the mountains resound with the noise of clashing horns. This fighting is an efficient way of sorting out the 'men' from the 'boys', as only mature males with large horns can win and this corresponds with the ability to sire and protect many offspring. The defeated males, although they may be sexually mature, must wait their turn, until their horns grow and they are able to defend a harem and

A pair of white and woolly Rocky Mountain goats disturbed on a rugged mountainside eye the intruder suspiciously.

young. The victors gather a large herd of females, although up to a fifth remain barren; perhaps in the world of the ibex it is status-worthy to collect as many females as possible irrespective of whether the male can mate with all of them. The young ibex are born in May and begin to graze after a month, but are not weaned until autumn.

The ibex poses a problem to the zoologist: how many species are there? Some people claim that there are only five. Two animals are of the same species if they remain distinct in the wild without the formation of mixed or hybrid population. Most ibex live in different regions and so have little chance to interbreed. Bringing different species together in captivity does not solve the problem because artificial conditions often force the animals to behave in an unnatural way. Evidence from cave paintings in western Europe does show us, however, that during the last ice age Spanish and alpine ibex lived together but did not interbreed. In the southern slopes of the Caucasus in Russia it seems that hybrids do occur between forms known as the Kuban tur and Daghestan tur. This situation may arise because a strong male of one species, unable to form a harem of his own, will drive off a weaker male of the other species and take over his harem. The offspring of these mixed marriages are, however, infertile. There is no continuing hybrid population. From this evidence it seems that there are several distinct species of ibex in Europe and Asia.

The male ibex is a distinguished beast, but the markhor is an even more impressive animal and can be considered as the king of all the wild goats. It is the largest and most powerfully built of them all. Apart from its size the male has large, spiral, backwardly-directed horns and both sexes have a large beard. Many markhor have different coloured coats and horn shapes, but unlike the ibex

An angry male alpine ibex makes a lunge at a rival over the heads of two other members of the herd.

they are not different species and represent races of *Capra falconeri*. The name markhor is derived from the Persian meaning snake-eater. Over a century ago a travelling naturalist wrote that the Afghans also referred to this animal as snake-eater, for they believe that it deliberately seeks out and eats snakes. For that reason also, they believe that if a man is bitten by a snake he can be cured by eating the flesh of the markhor. Markhors live on the sides of deep rocky gorges in Kashmir, Pakistan and across the border into Russia. They are not found at such high altitudes as the ibex, but prefer to live dangerously at a lower level, scrambling along the sides of precipitous gorges.

The behaviour of this animal is little understood, but from the facts known, the rut and other reproductive behaviour follow the same lines as those of the ibex. The male markhor show clockwork timing in their downward migration for the rut. In the Hindu Kush region the males regularly appear on December 14, whatever the weather.

A goat-like sheep

The mouflon is the only European wild sheep. The horns are usually found on the males only and form a close spiral with the tips sometimes curving slightly inwards. There is no gland at the base of the tail as in the closely related wild goats. The mouflon is found as a truly wild animal only in Corsica and Sardinia but has been successfully introduced into other mountainous parts of Europe. In its reproductive behaviour an interesting appeasement ceremony has been observed among males. After the fight for the female the winner may present his neck to be licked by the loser. He will sometimes go down on his knees to do this. Although he is obviously the stronger, this is a gesture of submission on the part of the victor. It can be interpreted as a sign of friendliness, and as a ritual end to the fight. This harmless abasement probably serves to reduce aggression among males of the herd in much the same way as does shaking hands or bowing after organized combat between men.

Conservation conflict

To people concerned with the conservation of natural areas, wild goats and sheep often represent an unwanted pest. This attitude is hardly surprising, for the goats have been responsible for the devastation of large areas of land, especially around the Mediterranean. They will eat most kinds of vegetation, and where the land is

31

susceptible to long periods of drought followed by heavy rain it soon becomes eroded and loses its valuable topsoil. Although the wild goat and sheep are not the main culprits today (they have been replaced by ignorant farmers), they probably helped in this spoilage, for many mountain types once lived at lower altitudes and have only recently moved into the mountains to avoid man's persecution. Mountain goats are thus fairly safe from man in their mountain retreats, although they are preyed upon by the wolf and eagle. There is, however, a growing danger from hunters. Despite protective measures taken by many countries a few species are now on the danger list. The Cyprian mouflon *Ovis orientalis ophion* is a race of the Asiatic mouflon or red sheep. This animal is found only on the island of Cyprus. During the Middle Ages, when this animal was very common, it was hunted with hounds, even with cheetahs; its flesh has always been esteemed by the islanders. More recently, due to an increase of the island's population with corresponding developments in industry and agriculture, this mouflon has suffered more serious losses. By 1937 it was estimated that no more than fifteen individuals remained in their last stronghold, the Paphos forest in the southwest corner of the island. Since then the entire forest comprising nearly 150,000 acres has been declared a game reserve in which the carrying of firearms is strictly prohibited.

Perhaps the most important protective measure taken has been the exclusion of all domesticated goats from the

Left. French Alps billie-goats. Domestic goats are kept by mountain villagers the world over as they can survive on poor vegetation and still provide milk, cheese and meat.

Below. A young klipspringer, an African antelope of rocky mountainous regions, is fully developed at birth, able to stand within a few minutes and can run within two days.

forest, and with them the herdsmen, who have been primarily responsible for shooting the mouflon.

Another threatened species is the Walia ibex. This animal is the Ethiopian representative of the European ibex. It is the largest and most powerfully built of all the ibex species. Today it is confined to a narrow belt of precipitous crags and ledges in the Simien mountains of Ethiopia, a habitat that has been described as the most spectacular of its kind anywhere in the world.

The history of the Walia ibex is one of constant persecution. Local tribesmen hunt it for meat, hides and horn, the latter being used as drinking vessels. Most drastic of all has been the destruction of the animal's habitat. Even in the high mountains, steeply sloping land is cultivated for cereal crops. The land is also grazed by sheep and cattle which roam the high plateaux and much of the highland vegetation has been cut for fuel. Although plans have been drawn up to protect the ibex, little has been done to enforce them and its fate remains unsure.

A shaggy misfit

Tahr are like old men of the mountains, shaggy animals related to the sheep and goats but having odd characters all of their own. They have long tufts of hair on the elbows and jaws but lack the goat-like beard. Like goats they have no glands on the face and between the hooves, but there are glands under the tail, which in the male give off a strong smell, especially in the breeding season. There are three races of tahr, living in widely separated areas; the Arabian peninsula, southern India, and the Himalayas.

The Himalayan race are some of the world's most inaccessible animals. They live in the most craggy and precipitous places but never above the tree line, at ten to twelve thousand feet. The southern Indian form lives at a lower level but in similar terrain. Early this century about a dozen animals were sent from a breeding stock in England to New Zealand. They were released near Mount Cook on South Island and have since spread over much of the southern alps. It is interesting to find that the tahr has adapted perfectly to the reversed seasons of the southern hemisphere. They still mate in the winter, although it is May and June in their new habitat, and give birth in the summer, December. The habitat does differ, however, from their original home. It is more snowy and considerably more fertile. For this reason the tahr are found at lower altitudes during the winter, and because of the more luxuriant vegetation they reach much larger sizes. Old males of 300 pounds have been recorded and ewes may reach up to 100 pounds, weights of a third more than in their natural home. Although the population is expanding and successful, natural selection still take its toll: four-fifths of each year's young die by the end of the third winter, leaving only a fifth to breed.

Both goat and antelope

Roaming the mountains of Asia are three types of goat-antelope, the serow, goral and takin, animals that bear some resemblance to both the goats and antelopes. The three species of serow live in areas ranging from Sumatra and Malaya to the Himalayas, Japan and Formosa. Serow prefer the humid gorges of small streams from two to eight thousand feet. Unlike mountain goats, they are solitary animals forming individual territories which are patrolled by the occupier and defended vigorously against intruders of the same species. Serow feed at dawn and dusk, preferring to retire into the dense undergrowth during the heat of the day. Their courtship behaviour resembles that of goats and gazelles. The male licks the female's mouth, strikes between her hindlegs with his forelegs as she walks away and rubs his horns against her genitalia. Serow fall victim to many types of animal hunters for the foothills where they live are also the home of many predators; leopards, tigers, wild dogs and wolves – life for the serow is one of constant danger.

A close relative of the serow is the goral, which like its larger cousin has a pair of small, backward-directed horns. There are three distinct species. The rarest, the brown goral, is known from only one specimen found in the dry country of the Upper Brahmaputra in south-eastern Tibet. Goral occupy a variety of habitats in different parts of their range. For example, the grey goral lives in Szechwan in the steep-sided, often vertical gorges of big rivers. The vegetation consists of short grass and thorn-bushes such as juniper, barberry and rose. At higher altitudes it lives in the valleys of small mountain torrents. This terrain is characterized by a series of steep gorges interspersed with areas of dense vegetation. In the northern part of its range the goral lives in quite a different kind of habitat. Here it frequents grassland areas, thickets of deciduous trees and boulder-strewn slopes.

Like the goat it is a great opportunist and will take a wide variety of foodstuffs. In summer goral graze low-lying vegetation but as autumn comes they migrate to more forested areas where they eat mainly leaves and nuts which they root out with their snouts. In February and March when the snowfall is greatest they exist on a diet of branches. After their morning feed when the weather is fine, goral like to sunbathe on rock ledges with their feet tucked under their bodies and their heads stretched out.

Until 1961, only two species of goral were known, although there were many reports of a red-coated animal being seen in Asian hills. It was not until a man sent a rug to the British Museum to be identified that the third species, the red goral, was discovered.

The takin is the largest of the goat-antelopes. Its horns are its most outstanding feature; they are fibrous, with thickened bases rather like those of a musk ox. The coat colour varies with the sexes. The colour of the males is a dull yellow, the females are greyish and the young are black. Takin live mainly in China, on the steep slopes of the mountains above 7,000 feet. Here the ground is covered with mountain forest and dense thickets of bamboo and rhododendron. Takin cut regular paths through this jungle along which they travel to and from their feeding grounds. In summer the takin emerge from the protection of the undergrowth to feed in the open dwarf bush zone above 10,000 feet.

The takin is something of a mystery animal to zoologists. Remains have been found from the Pleistocene period, a million years ago, that differ little from the living animal and so give us little indication of the animal's ancestry. Several experts on the hoofed mammals have proposed that the closest relative of the takin is the musk ox. Both animals are stockily built with strong, thick limb-bones and both have similarly shaped fibrous horns. In both, also, there are no face glands as in the chamois, and the lateral hooves are very large. Against this, others have pointed out that the takin lacks many features possessed by the musk ox, like the asymmetrical hooves and the long, sway-backed, concave spine which is very different from the convex, almost hump-back of the takin. They also point out that when

Opposite; top. *Alpine ibex at rest in the sun; its choice of accommodation is silent witness to its agility.*
Bottom. *Klipspringer in typical tiptoe stance. So sure-footed is this South African antelope that it was given this Afrikaans name, which means rock-jumper.*
Overleaf; left. *The grey goral is a rare goat-antelope which is being bred in a west Himalayan sanctuary. The natural home is in Szechwan, where the animal frequents the steep, arid gorges of rivers like the Yangtse, and high mountain valleys at altitudes of up to 13,500 feet.*
Top right. *Bighorn sheep forage on the snow-covered slopes of the North American Rockies in winter.*
Bottom right. *Male Himalayan tahr; the female is without the mane which distinguishes him.*
Page 40. *A grizzly bear among Alaskan peaks. This brown bear is quite at home amid snow and ice, and often toboggans down slopes instead of bothering to walk.*

the much heavier horns are taken into account the skull closely resembles that of the serow and goral.

There are few definite facts. Certainly, the takin, serow and goral belong to the little-known group closely related to both the sheep and antelopes. All three animals belong to an old relict group that is found either in mountainous regions, or like the musk ox, in the far north. Most of the living forms seem to have their own, long, separate history and have gradually been forced into smaller and more remote areas due to competition from their more successful cousins, the sheep and goats.

A European equivalent

Europe, too, has a goat-antelope, the chamois, which lives in the Pyrenees, Alps and Appenines and ranges into Asia Minor and the Caucasus. Chamois live among the steep rocks and cliffs of mountain slopes between five and six thousand feet, reaching up to the snowline in summer and eating grass, sparse mountain lichens and herbage. Chamois are shy and elusive and are remarkably alert. They have excellent powers of sight and hearing and, even for mountain animals, are extremely agile. A chamois can leap thirteen feet upwards and make a long jump of over twenty-three feet. The jarring effect of these huge leaps across bare rock surfaces would be tremendous, but the chamois has its own shock-absorbing system. The lower legs act as springs and when the chamois lands heavily the 'spring-heels' contract, bearing the brunt of this sturdy animal's weight. Folklore has it that the chamois' horns, some ten inches long and curved

Point of balance: an alert klipspringer on a downward move. It has been claimed that this small antelope can land on a point no bigger than one inch in diameter.

41

1

Master portraits

1. The mouflon's horns may attain a length of up to 34 inches, distinguishing it from domestic cousins.

2. Snow still clinging to his face, a bighorn sheep pauses to survey the scene.

3. Carried by the female as well as the male, the horns of the maned serow are small and inconspicuous.

4. The ibex, surefooted goat of the mountains of Europe and Asia, closely resembles the domestic goat in its face.

5. The chamois is famed for its leaping prowess, keen hearing and eyesight.

6. When they are fully-grown, the horns of this alpine ibex will become scimitar-shaped.

backwards at the end, serve the same purpose. They are reputed to absorb shock and save the animal from death should it fall head-first down a precipice.

Buck chamois are usually solitary except during the rut. The females and young stay together in groups but

merge into vast herds during the mating season. Chamois kids follow the does almost from birth and learn their mountaineering skills very swiftly by jumping on and off their mothers' backs.

Chamois have a much-coveted coat of long hair with

Mother chamois watch the photographer while a kid watches the track's edge. Kids follow the does from birth and soon climb.

thick underfur. This is tawny in summer and darker brown to black in winter and is both warm and protective. Hunters, however, find it difficult to track and kill this sharp and nimble mountain animal and its main enemies are foxes and eagles which occasionally prey on the young.

Statuesque jumpers

The klipspringer is a small African antelope, which like the chamois of the northern hemisphere is adapted to life on bare and inaccessible rocky places. This three foot-long antelope has a thick wavy coat, each hair on the upper part is banded yellow and black giving the animal a pepper and salt effect. It also has a pair of short, sharp horns which stick straight up from the front of its head.

Home to the klipspringer means cliff ravines, rocky promontories, kopjes and the surrounding bush. It is seldom found far from rocks. The klipspringer has been tracked up to a height of 14,800 feet on Mount Elgon in Kenya. The characteristic pose of this perky little antelope is to stand with its head held up and with all four feet together, alert and rigid. The hooves on the forelegs are elongated, giving the impression that the animal stands on the tips of its toes like a ballet dancer. The klipspringer is such a charming animal that is has become the national animal of South Africa. Its name, which is Afrikaans for rock jumper, is quite justified. It has an amazing capacity for jumping from crag to crag, and is more surefooted than any mountain goat, bouncing up almost perpendicular cliffs like a rubber ball then dropping down a sheer rock face without losing a foothold. A South African naturalist once observed a leap of thirty feet from the edge of a rocky precipice onto a jutting ledge below, whereupon the antelope steadied itself for a moment, then ran at a fast pace obliquely down the mountain.

Apart from its agility the only other protection the klipspringer has is the curious texture of its coat, which is so brittle that if the animal is caught, the hairs come away in the predator's mouth and the klipspringer escapes. The lost hair is soon replaced by new growth. The coat must also have a cushioning effect against thorn bushes and sharp rocks. At one time these animals were so abundant that their hair was used for stuffing saddles and mattresses, but today the story is quite different for the klipspringers are on the decline. It seems that the antelopes can only live in very restricted areas; if persecuted in these regions they are unable to adapt elsewhere and this often leads to local extinction. At present there are fair numbers of these animals in localized regions.

Bears, cats and yetis

Hushed, cruel, amber-eyed.
Before the time of the danger of the day.
Or at dusk on the boulder-broken mountainside
The great cats seek their prey.

from 'Pumas' by George Sterling

The magnificent bears, the enigmatic panda
and the rare snow leopard are some of the big
mammals persecuted by man which have found
refuge in the mountains. Perhaps they hold the
key to the 'abominable snowman' mystery, but
a satisfactory answer to this fascinating riddle
of the Himalayas has yet to be found.

The larger an animal is, the more acute becomes the mountains' lack of hospitality. Much energy is needed to find food through the obstructions of difficult terrain, possibly snow and the added handicaps of extreme temperatures and pressure. A large animal has more body to support, keep warm and move about, and therefor needs more energy – food. The mountains have only a limited supply, at least in the upper reaches. The severity of winter in the heights prevents most species living there permanently, but there are many which exploit the lower, warmer levels in winter, or hibernate, and hunt the upper levels in summer.

Of the large plant-eating mammals, the goats, sheep, antelopes, yaks and llamas have conquered the heights and manage to exist with only slight seasonal adjustment.

The rodents, as everywhere, have managed to populate most mountains. Due to their small size and hibernating habits, they stand up well to the conditions, and profit by the safety they gain in inaccessibility.

The safety is not, however, complete. Persecuted away from lowland homes, or adapted to a life of cold, there are a few predators to exploit the food sources presented by these animals. Perhaps the most familiar predator is the bear. In one form or another it has populated most of the mountains of the world.

A grizzly's grasp on a gravid salmon causes her eggs to spurt forth. Many salmon are flipped or seized from the shallows by bears using their paws or jaws and are so prevented from returning to their ancestral birthplaces to breed.

Bears sleep for survival

The most widespread of the bears is the brown bear. It is a matter of opinion, almost a matter of taste, whether one considers the grizzlies, and the immense Kodiak and Kenai bears as the same species as the European, Russian, and Syrian bears, but all have roughly the same habits. At their largest the brown bears are nine feet long and about 1,700 pounds weight. They are heavily built, and have large paws. The claws cannot be retracted, so the usual track has the imprints of claws leading it.

Brown bears live in wild, mountainous country as well as in forests, wandering about singly or in family parties. Their home range is usually about forty miles wide, but some may wander beyond this. Canadian mountains are sometimes decorated with bear trails up one side, bear toboggan runs down the other, where a hungry grizzly has gone in search of richer hunting grounds. For all their size, only wounded or nursing bears will attack man. But when they do, the results are usually fatal.

The bear's diet is, at first sight, surprising for so large and apparently savage an animal. It will eat almost anything, from bison and farmstock if its journeys take it near the plains, to berries, fruit and roots. Honey,

the grubs of wild bees, insects, deer and often fish form parts of its meals. When salmon are running in chill mountain streams, the bears have a field day standing in the shallows and flipping them to the shore with a fore-paw. It is perhaps this adaptability of diet, combined with its life history, that has adapted the bear so perfectly to mountains.

Summer is, to a brown bear, a time to fatten up, even overfeed, in preparation for the winter. Then, with the onset of colder weather, it finds a den among the rocks, in a hollow tree, or even digs one in the earth of the hillside, and goes to sleep until spring, existing on stored fat within the body. In January or February, in the worst part of the winter, the cubs are born. They are very small indeed: about eight inches long and one and a half pounds weight. The mother rouses herself just enough to lick them clean, then the happy family sleep until spring. This process overcomes two problems at once; the bear does not have to forage in the almost impossible winter, and the young are born and go through the first stages of development in the warmth of a den, then have spring and summer for further development. They are then fit to face the rigours of hibernation themselves.

Bear facts and fallacies

Above. *Spectacled bear portraits. Although there is only one species of South American spectacled bear there are innumerable facial markings from complete rings to stripes over the nose. It is the only bear that is to be found in the Southern Hemisphere.*

Left. *Himalayan black bear of south-east Asian mountains in a threatening pose, reveals its white new moon crescent chest marking which also names it moon bear. Its habits are similar to the brown bear.*

Above right. *An American black bear illustrates that a bear's diet is not just meat such as young deer, ground birds and rodents. Much of its intake is made up of berries, fruits, birds' eggs and insects. Here it digs out grubs, larvae and insects from a rotting log.*

The brown bears are classic examples of animals which, through adaptability, have found refuge in the mountains. Throughout their range, and particularly in Europe and America, they have been shot, trapped and hunted for a variety of reasons. Numbers of grizzlies have been seriously depleted, and the European brown bear was even, in the early 1960s, considered extinct. A few do, however, remain, not surprisingly in forest uplands. There are a few pockets of them in the Pyrenees and in Scandinavia, and slightly larger numbers in eastern Europe.

Of the black bears, the most predominantly mountain-living is the Himalayan. About 6½ feet long, with black fur and a white crescent on the chest, it lives in high forest and brush from the Himalayas to Korea and Formosa, and has a race on Kyushu, Japan. In summer it ventures as high as 11,000 feet, descending to about 4,000 in winter. Like many other bears it is solitary, even to the extent of ignoring any neighbours it meets on its travels. In the manner of the brown bear it has a home range, which consists of many well-trodden paths and regularly visited spots for feeding, drinking, resting and sunbathing.

In summer it builds a nest of sticks in a tree from which to catch the sun, in winter it does the same on snow. Unlike the brown bears, it has no set hibernation. It goes into short sleeping periods if a winter is exceptionally severe. The fur, however, compensates for this lack of escape from the cold. In summer it is quite sparse, but in winter it becomes thick and long. Unlike most cold-climate animals, the Himalayan black bear has quite large ears. What advantage they confer is not known, but they are well-furred to prevent heat loss. The young are born also in a winter den.

Again like the brown bear, the black bear is nearly omnivorous; in fact, it tends towards the vegetarian, eating berries, nuts, honey, and any standing crops it comes across. But the bear is considered one of the main enemies of the Kashmir stag, being blamed for taking young animals. Some have been seen to kill lambs and ponies.

Having little fear of man, the Himalayan black bear has acquired a reputation for ferocity. This has probable foundation in the fact that, unlike other bears, it does not shuffle away at the first signs – scent or sound – of man. Thus there are more face to face encounters, since men use bear tracks and vice versa, than with other bears, and consequently the attack rate goes up. Because of its obvious strength it is respected, even held sacred, by the people living in its range. The Chinese prize the flesh and bones as medicaments and aphrodisiacs, and the Ainu of Japan feature it in their religious festivals. Man seems, so far, to have made little impression on the numbers of this animal.

A young panda is cradled in its mother's arms. This one was born at Peking Zoo where artificial insemination is practised in breeding pandas. Very little is known about the panda's breeding habits in the wild but obviously zoo-born animals will boost the small population number.

Pandas and publicity

Sharing an ancestor with the bears, the pandas also share a preference for mountains. The first animal to be given the name 'panda' was the cat-bear or red panda from the mountain forests of Nepal, Sikkim and Upper Burma. As its more widely accepted name implies, it has a mixed external appearance. Its body is about two feet long and it has a 22-inch brush-like tail. It is covered with rich, woolly fur, and has a striped, raccoon-like tail – it is classed by zoologists in the same family.

The cat-bear spends its time in trees at altitudes of seven to twelve thousand feet, and is quite common. It seems little at home on the ground, walking with an awkward pigeon-toed gait, but it spends a lot of time there. Morning and evening are the main feeding times, and it is then that a tendency marked among the bears, towards vegetarianism, shows itself to the full. Despite a set of teeth that do credit to a specialist meat-eater and a general body shape associated with animal-foraging creatures like raccoons, the cat-bear is probably wholly vegetarian. It feeds on leaves and fruits, coming down from the trees in the morning and evening. The rest of its time is spent curled, cat-like, in a crotch of a tree.

To call the cat-bear a panda in modern times would cause a great deal of confusion; the press coverage given

Although appearing to be on friendly terms in this picture An-an from Moscow Zoo, and Chi-chi, from London Zoo, never mated. Two unsuccessful attempts were made. One in 1966 when Chi-chi visited An-an and again in 1968–69 when An-an spent ten months with Chi-chi in London Zoo.

The legend of the yeti

1. *A Nepalese official holds the 'yeti scalp' around which there was much controversy in 1960. It was said to be over one hundred years old and a priceless religious relic. Sir Edmund Hillary exhibited the cap in the U.S.A. and in London and Paris. After investigation of the hairs of the cap it was found to be a 'fake'. The hairs were from a serow, a goat-antelope. It was never discovered if the cap was a genuine relic or an imitation of one.*

2. *The famous tracks on the Menlung Tsu Glacier, Everest, photographed by Eric Shipton in 1951. The tracks were made by a bipedal (two-footed) animal but no satisfactory explanation could be given about them.*

3. *These are the most recently seen yeti tracks. They were photographed by Don Whillans while on the 1970 Annapurna Expedition. One March evening Whillans saw an object with arms and legs that looked like a cross between a gorilla and a bear. The Sherpas were certain he had seen a yeti.*

4. *The footprints of a snow leopard seen at 14,000 feet.*

5. *Imprint of the left foot of a yeti from Nepal. The pick indicates size.*

6. *Bear tracks have been the centre of yeti confusion in the past. These are of the brown bear. It has a large sole and five toes of equal size, and claws. In fact the tracks are very different from those photographed by Shipton and Whillans.*

5

6

to the attempted mating of the captive giant pandas Chi-chi and An-an has probably never been equalled for any other animal. The animal that has taken the name is a six-foot stockily-built creature, with black legs, ears, eye-patches and shoulders, with the rest white. It lives on the cold, damp hillsides of eastern Tibet and south-west China. Solitary animals, pandas are still much shrouded in mystery, but they show familiar habits. They are nearly omnivorous, despite early belief that they fed only on bamboo shoots. They eat grasses, gentian and crocus flowers, small rodents, small birds, and fishes flipped, bear-like, from streams. Whether or not pandas are rare is a matter for conjecture. They were always inaccessible geographically, and now the Chinese government makes their study by foreigners impossible. If their numbers are low, then it may be because of indiscriminate and often inefficient collecting for zoos and exhibitions, for the animal is obviously attractive.

The Yeti – legend or life

If any animal, apart from the coelacanth fish, can boast almost as much publicity as the panda, it must be the alleged abominable snowman. This hairy denizen of the Tibetan and Nepalese mountain slopes has been the centre of some of the most bitter 'does-it-exist-or-not?' arguments of modern times. As far as the popular Western World is concerned, the story starts with Eric Shipton's sixth attempt at climbing Everest, in 1951. While exploring a neighbouring range, the Guari Sankar, he and two companions came upon a trail of enormous, human-looking footprints in the snow. They followed the trail until it was lost in a moraine of ice. The prints were more than a foot long, and a man on the

Opposite; top. *A North American mountain lion, also known as the puma or cougar, cleans a paw whilst a grizzly bear tucks into the remains of a kill.*
Bottom. *The hungry-looking timber wolf of Europe, Asia and North America covers long distances in wild country in the endless hunt for prey.*
Overleaf. *Grizzly bears welcome a change of diet in the shape of salmon running upriver to spawn. These big carnivores are surprisingly skilful fishermen.*
Page 60. *The original panda. Discovered and named before its larger black and white cousin, the cat-bear has had many names: fox-cat, fire-fox and red panda are a few, but the name cat-bear has proved most useful to distinguish it from the giant panda. The cat-bear lives in the forests of the eastern Himalayas, feeding almost exclusively on leaves and fruit, although its teeth are those of a meat-eater.*

same scale would stand about eight feet high. Previous Everest expeditions had seen similar prints, even animals in the distance.

Legends of wild hairy men of the mountains are widespread; few countries with inaccessible, high, and mysterious places fail to populate them with diabolical creatures, preferably man-eating. Of all of them, however, the abominable snowman, or yeti, seems the best documented. Belief in yetis is universal among the natives of the mountains, and it is certain that, whatever the cause, some animal with large feet makes a regular habit of going to quite great heights – one set of tracks was found at 23,000 feet. Because of the way it walks, the local race of brown bear leaves what is at first sight a two-legged track. The closeup photograph taken by Shipton, however, seems to refute any bear theory; the big toe is too pronounced and there are no claw marks. Reports from natives are hundredfold, most of them alleging to be first-hand. Scalps have been kept as sacred objects in villages, and photographed, only to be dismissed as fakes by experts.

The most recent report comes from the 1970 Annapurna expedition. On March 25, Don Whillans, deputy leader of the British climbing expedition, set up a lone reconnaissance camp on Machchapuchhare. As he lay in his tent on a moonlit night he saw something moving. In the shadow he could make out the arms and legs of the

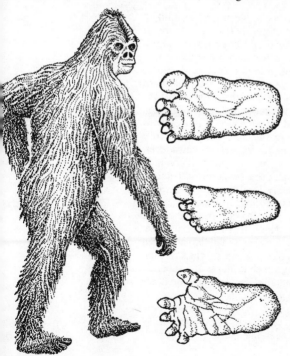

Is this what the Abominable Snowman looks like? – it is a possible reconstruction. But few people claim to have seen a yeti; most explorers come across large human-like footprints in the snow. The sole of the foot of a yeti (top) *drawn from an imprint in snow shows just how human-like it is, especially when compared with the sole of a gorilla's hindfoot* (bottom) *and a man's sole* (middle).

object, which went right across a snow ridge at a height of twelve to thirteen thousand feet. He described it as looking 'like a cross between a bear and a gorilla'. The sherpas, when told of this sighting, assured him that he had seen a yeti, probably a young one.

The size of the animal, judged from all the tracks and accounts, seems to preclude any possibility of its being any of the native high-dwelling monkeys or apes. Distributions, too, do not seem to tally. One view is that the yeti is a relict ape species, backwatered by evolution in its perfect inaccessible home and adaptable enough to exploit it. One would like to think so, but as with the panda, information has virtually ceased to come out of this politically inflammable area, and attempts to gain entry permission from the relevant governments are met with stony silence.

The adaptable cats

One of the least credible explanations offered for the tracks on the snow was that they were made by the rare snow leopard. Apart from leaving a fourlegged track which looks like that of an overgrown cat, the animal is so rare that the profusion of tracks found by yeti-hunting expeditions would have gladdened the heart of many an animal lover.

The snow leopard is certainly the most beautiful of mountain dwellers, if not of the whole cat family. It measures about four feet head and body length, with a thick, furry, three-foot tail. It has long, thick fur, with a dense, woolly underfur. The ground colour is whitish or greyish, with a pattern of rosettes on the upperparts. In summer the leopards live at or near the snow line of the central Asian highlands at about twelve to thirteen thousand feet, being forced by winter back to as low as 6,000 feet. They rest during the day, becoming active during the evening, searching for wild sheep, musk deer, rodents and domestic stock such as goats. Very little more is known of the animal, due to widespread persecution for its fur, and probably local extinction. Experts estimate that only about 400 of these creatures remain in the whole Himalayan complex. As an example of the perfect snow predator, the snow leopard stands supreme. Thickly furred, even to its counterpoise tail, large-padded for grip on snow, lightly-coloured and patched to look like the snowy rocks among which it hunts, and superbly agile, it is one of the mountains' few full-time predator occupants.

In sharp contrast with this extreme specialization, another member of the cat family has successfully exploited the mountains. It is the puma or cougar. A

widespread cat, it has adapted itself to nearly every available American habitat. It ranges from western Canada to the southern half of South America, on mountains, plains, deserts and in forests. Such is its prowess in the mountains, however, that an alternative name is mountain lion.

From four to eight feet long, of which three-eighths is tail, and of yellowish-brown colour, it looks very like a lioness. As one would judge from its build, it is a remarkably powerful creature; it is easy work for prey of three times the cat's weight, like a deer, to be thrown over the shoulder and dragged away. Its agility too, is remarkable; it can regularly cover 20 feet at a bound, and a leap of 40 feet has been recorded. It can jump upwards about 15 feet, and drop to earth from 60. Like many other cats, it leads a solitary life, wandering in search of prey. It has a hunting ground of about 20–30 miles wide, and its trails are marked with lightly buried prey.

Puma prey mainly on deer; if puma are killed off in any given area, the deer multiply rapidly. It also takes a variety of small animals, including porcupines. It sometimes attacks domestic stock, such as sheep or goats, as well as horses and cattle, and will take carrion. Ponies are said to be particularly favoured. Pumas stalk their larger prey, suddenly pouncing on their backs with a powerful leap and biting for the spine. Puma breed in the lowlands, and have no fixed season for it. They have few enemies apart from man. Jaguars, grizzlies and wolverines will fight with them, but this is probably direct competition for food and living space. If food is abundant, they should live in harmony.

The puma is one of the adaptable cats; its agility, strength and hunting ability make it at home nearly anywhere in America. It is, however, among the rocks and loose scrub of mountain slopes that it excels.

Predator for preservation

Persistently sought after and hunted for its supreme and beautiful fur above the treeline in its high mountain homes of Central Asia, the snow leopard has good adaptations for surviving in the environment. Thick fur even to its long tail gives insulation, large padded feet give easy movement in the snow, whitish spotted fur for hiding and small ears to prevent too much heat loss.

63

The most savage cat

There is no direct equivalent of the puma in Europe. All the large predators have been the victims of intensive persecution, and only two cats remain, the lynx and the wildcat. The lynx is an animal of the woodlands, but the wildcat has found sanctuary in the mountains. Looking like a large domestic tabby, the wildcat is about two feet long, with a record of three feet nine inches. It has a thick, short, bushy tail ringed with black and ending in a black tip. It lives in the mountains of Europe, especially in the Balkans, and has an isolated population in Scotland, which is said to be increasing.

The wildcat lives on lonely mountainsides, having a home range of up to 175 acres, which the male defends against other wildcats. It may wander far beyond these boundaries in search of food or a mate. In defence of its range, its mate or its litter, the wildcat is size for size the most savage of all the cats, and, in the breeding season, will attack any intruder, no matter what its size, with remarkable ferocity. Although normally a dawn and dusk hunter, it will prowl all day during the autumn, and likes to bask in the sun on exposed boughs or rocky ledges.

There is some confusion between the wildcat and the domestic cats which turn wild. This is understandable; both are equally ferocious, and after a few generations, most domestic cats revert to the basic tabby coloration.

The true wildcat is a classic example of persecution by man. It has few enemies in its home, but a taste for poultry, game and the occasional lamb have ensured

Known for its remarkable strength and stamina, a puma is also called cougar or mountain lion. When hunting (right) it may travel up to 50 miles. Deer is the most prefered food but it will also kill smaller prey such as a rabbit (above) if the chance presents itself. Rarely exceeding eight feet in length and 250 lb in weight it is a formidable carnivore, ranging from western Canada to Patagonia in the southern half of South America on plains, mountains, deserts and forests.

that every farming man's hand is against it. The cat also eats mountain hares, and is capable of killing a roe deer fawn. Many years ago, when it was infinitely more widespread, the wildcat was hunted for sport.

It has two breeding seasons, in early March and in May, marked by the insane and bone-chilling screams of the male as he tries to attract a mate. The female builds a nest in the most remote spot she can find, and drives away the male, for he is given to eating the babies. The usual litter is four or five kittens, all of which are as intractable and savage as the mother. Although some people have claimed success in taming these creatures, they are on the whole completely untameable. Scientific opinion agrees that they are probably not the ancestors of the domestic cat, for all the apparent similarities.

All the mountain predators have suffered to some extent from persecution. Some, like the wildcat, puma and bear survive only in the inaccessible parts of their former ranges. This situation is not altogether bad; they have found in the heights homes which will ensure their survival for many years to come. It remains only for attitudes towards furs to change a little and even the snow leopard could once more become common.

Beautiful but savage: the European wildcat resembles the domesticated tabby but it is more heavily built. In Britain due to persecution it has retreated to the Highlands of Scotland and in continental Europe chief strongholds are mountains, especially the Balkans.

Close to the ground

In the snow-furred sedge,
Couches the white hare;
Her stronghold is there.

Who cheated the loud pack,
Biting steel, poacher's sack;
Among the steep rocks
Outwitted the fanged fox.

from 'The White Hare' by Lilian Bowes Lyon

Insignificant though they may be in size the
many rodents and other small furry mammals
play a very important part in the mountain
economy. These eaters of ground vegetation
are a vital link in the food chain falling prey to
stoats, foxes and eagles. Among them are the
chinchilla and the migratory lemming.

All over the world, wherever there is food in the form of plants, the gnawing animals have spread and diversified. They are in the desert; jerboas, gerbils and spiny mice eke a living from desert plants and scarcely, if ever, drink. Rats and mice outnumber humans in most centres of civilization, and in the countryside farmers fight a never-ending battle with them and rabbits. Squirrels live in the trees of tropical and temperate forests and giant rats infest bamboo. Hares live well inside the Arctic circle. The list is long, and it is not surprising to find that little gnawing animals have found their way up mountains.

Small enough to lose little heat through their fur, and agile enough to make homes of burrows and crevices where temperatures are more equable, they are of a general pattern that adapts readily to cold. Most of them spend the winter sleeping and all have many babies, rapidly replacing losses to predators and conditions.

Since higher slopes are apt to become progressively steeper, rain and melting snow carry away more and more soil with increasing altitude. Eventually, soil deep enough for large trees and shrubs to grow cannot accumulate. Many plants are unable to survive without their shelter, so vegetation becomes abruptly sparse and conditions are much harsher.

Except for its black ear tips the Alpine hare sports a white coat in winter. It is easy to see the advantages of this.

Not usually connected with mountains, but neverthe-less a fairly common inhabitant, is the rabbit. An animal of the lowland meadows, it is so adaptable that it manages to exploit the sparse vegetation of the highlands. Here it serves a vital function; like many small animals, it is the basic diet of many predators, especially the eagles. The numbers of these hunters even vary with the number of rabbits available in any year. Close to the rabbit and often confused with it, the hare is another prey species of the mountains. It has, however, adapted more to its surroundings. The alpine hare of Europe – the same species as the blue hare of Scotland – finds camouflage in a change of fur colour with the seasons. In summer it is brown, merging with the moss and lichen-covered boulders of its home. In winter, it is white and can barely be distinguished from the snow. Its alternative name of blue hare comes from the spring and autumn combination coat, when the two colours mix.

Hares and relations

The mountain range of North America forms a corridor of sub-Arctic conditions along which northern animals can spread. One of these is the snowshoe rabbit, which, despite its name, is technically a hare. Smaller than most hares, at only sixteen inches long, it does not burrow like a rabbit, and behaves in all ways like a hare. It, too, has different winter and summer coats, earning it an alterna-tive name of varying hare. The change of coat in these animals is governed by the hours of daylight available. If, under laboratory conditions, the available daylight is extended to about eighteen hours, a snowshoe rabbit's coat will turn brown, no matter how low the temperature may be. This hare also has an adaptation common in animals that live in snow. It has hairy mats on the soles of its feet – functioning as snowshoes – that spread its weight and make progress easier over soft snow.

Pikas are related to rabbits and hares, but are infinitely more adapted, particularly in their behaviour, to life in the mountains. Two species live in North America and twelve in Asia. The largest is a foot long, the smallest less than half this size. They look like rabbits or hares with shorter rounded ears, and the legs are all the same length. The feet are hairy – not the 'snowshoe' effect of the hare – having a short coat of hairs that gives grip on rocks. They are greyish brown, with the exception of the Asiatic pika, which is red.

Pikas live in a variety of habitats; on plains, in deserts, in forests, and on rocky mountain sides. One species lives on Mount Everest at a height of 17,500 feet – the highest altitude recorded for an observed wild mammal.

A snowshoe rabbit dozes in the winter sun (left). The hairy mats on the soles of its feet help it move over the snow. In contrast, an Alpine hare on the alert (below). It is also called the blue hare after its spring and autumn coat colour.

Rather than take to its heels when frightened, a pika will drop into the nearest crevice and keep still. On mountains it uses crevices and cavities for shelter, on plains it burrows.

It is interesting to note how the boulder-strewn slopes of mountains all over the world have become occupied by similar animals: the pika in Europe, Asia and America; the viscacha in the Andes; the gundi in North Africa and the hyrax in South Africa.

Although winters are very cold in all the pikas' ranges, they do not hibernate. Instead they have the remarkable habit of cutting vegetation with their chisel-like teeth, drying it in the sun, and storing it as winter fodder. A pika may travel several hundred feet from its home to cut herbs and grass, carrying these in its mouth to a chosen spot to dry, adding a fresh layer each day. Some climb into the lower branches of young trees to take green shoots. The dry fodder is stored under an overhanging shelf of rock. A single store may hold up to a bushel of hay. The pikas may eat other food in winter – they tunnel under the snow and nibble bark from trees – but the main food is the dry fodder. They feed in the early morning and late afternoon spending midday basking in the sun.

A trait peculiar to the rabbit order is that of refection – the consumption of faeces to provide essential vitamins. During the day a pika's droppings are small, green and dry. At night they are coated in a jelly-like layer which keeps them soft and wet. These are swallowed and kept in the stomach to be mixed with fresh food and redigested. The activity of the bacteria while the faeces are in the open forms vitamins essential to the animal's health, and without them, it will die in about three weeks.

If well fed, pikas are exceptionally resistant to cold, for it is not the cold which kills animals in winter but the shortage of food. As they have their food stores, pikas can survive even when the ground is covered in snow. They even sun themselves on rocks in temperatures of −17°C.

The pika breeds two or three times a year, between May and September, and the young are born naked and helpless on beds of dried grass. From one ounce weight – an adult weighs a pound – they reach full size in about seven weeks. They are heavily preyed upon by predators, from eagles to weasels.

The footprints left by the fore and hind feet of a common hare (below) contrast with the bizarre prints made by a snowshoe hare, and emphasize the large hairy soles of the latter which make running on snow much easier.

A population problem

Linked in many minds to visions of mass suicide, the lemming is a mountain animal of particular interest. As a prey species it ranks supreme and as an example of

71

population regulation it is almost unique. All twelve species are from four to six inches long, with thick fur, small ears, blunt muzzles and tiny tails. Most accounts centre around the Norwegian lemmings, which range across Norway, Sweden, Finland and northwest Russia. It lives at three to four thousand feet above sea level, above the typically European line of dwarf willows. In summer it occupies moist stony ground covered in sedges, willow shrub and dwarf birch. In winter it lives under the snow, protected from cold and enemies. It builds a rounded nest of grass, which is often left hanging when the snow melts. Because their food is moss, lichens and grasses, winter does not interrupt the lemmings' lives and they often continue to breed.

Lemmings, like many small rodents, are subject to wide fluctuations in numbers from year to year. They also share with their close relations the voles, cyclic rises and falls in numbers. This is due to the relationship between their high breeding rates and the available food. Females of both types may produce up to eighty young in a year. If food is abundant, all these offspring will breed, as well as their parents, and so on until plague proportions are reached; densities of up to 12,000 field voles have been recorded. Although masses like this attract many predators, even foxes, weasels, owls and hawks can make little impression on them. In voles, overcrowding results in lowered fertility. There is less food per head which, together with the proximity of too many other voles, makes them quarrelsome and inhibits breeding. Apart from mutual male-female rejection through fighting, the animals tend to destroy their own litters. The results of all these factors is a drastic fall in the population.

The combination of food supplies provided by good weather in both early spring and late autumn gives lemmings enough food and time for quite a large expansion of numbers. If a moderate winter keeps enough snow around the runs and nests to protect the young, then the population becomes too large for the food supply. The result is a general movement away from the mountain sides towards food in new valleys.

The legends of mass suicide lie in this march. It is said that the lemmings go to the sea, a large lake or a fjord, and simply swim out until they drown. It is true that lemmings cross water on migration, but this action is purely functional. They are good swimmers, but usually hesitate before entering water.

Observations by the Swedish naturalist Dr. Kai Curry-Lindahl in the lemming peak population of 1960 indicate that even this slight hesitation can be lost on migration. If an obstruction like a river causes numbers to become concentrated in one spot, tension among the lemmings builds up. The result is a kind of 'panic' in which the urge to move forwards becomes stronger than

When food is plentiful the little Norwegian lemming may produce up to eighty young in one year. Should the weather conditions remain favourable and the food abundant the lemming population becomes abnormally high. This is when the legendary migrations occur.

any reluctance to swim. A narrow stretch of water is easily crossed and the migration continues, but in too wide a stretch such as a fjord or an arm of the sea they will all drown.

If migration does not solve the crowding problem, the lemmings breed on the lower slopes. They eventually reach a point at which the stress and tension of over-population affect the internal balance of their bodies. The usual result is brain damage, exhaustion, and death. Thus the lemming habitat, never luxuriantly vegetated, is not over-exploited. Without these two mechanisms, one plague year would be enough to strip it bare.

The co-operative marmot

If any ground-living animal can be said to symbolize the mountains, it is the marmot. To anyone walking or climbing in the lower slopes of the Alps or the Himalayas, marmots appear with the regularity of rabbits in a rich lowland pasture. Members of the squirrel family, the sixteen species are found in the uplands of Alaska, most of Canada, the United States (except the extreme south), western Europe, and in all but the southerly parts of Asia. Although primarily animals of the upper elevations, they do occur on plains and prairies in some northerly areas.

The alpine marmot is typical; up to two feet long with a six-inch tail, it is a stocky, short-legged creature, weighing up to eighteen pounds. It lives in and around the treeline, between four and nine thousand feet.

Marmots live in burrows and crevices on boulder-strewn slopes, retreating by night to the straw nests built at their deepest points several yards down. By day, they have a well-established routine. As the first warmth of the sun falls on each burrow, the occupants emerge and spend the next hour sunning and grooming, after which they make their ways to feeding grounds. They eat grass, sedges, herbaceous plants, and some roots. Feeding lasts about two hours, then the animals return to grooming, sunning, and occasional digging. There is another feeding session in the last two or three hours of the day.

Although too large to fall prey to small carnivores like the stoat, marmots lose some of their numbers to eagles and foxes. Efficient alarm signals on the part of these rodents, however, restrict the losses to a minimum. The alarm cry is a shrill, high whistle, increasing in intensity as an intruder approaches. The idea that the marmots post sentries is popular, but the succession of whistles as one approaches a group of them is due to the fact that only the marmot nearest the intruder gives the alarm. Hearing two or three whistles, then seeing several retreating marmots, one could easily assume deliberate placing of sentries.

Animal predators are not the only ones to suffer from this warning efficiency. Like the chatter of an alarmed blackbird in the fields, or the scream of a jay in the woods, the marmots' cries alert their neighbours in the mountains. There can be few human hunters who have stalked shy mountain goats and chamois who have not, at one time or another, disturbed these alert rodents then seen their quarry disappear at high speed among the crags.

The yellow-bellied marmot, like all marmots, spends much of its day feeding. It lives low down the mountains of North America in burrows in the rocks.

Nearly lost to fashion

The marmot has little or no commercial value in its western range and proves an elusive quarry for anyone wishing to eat it in its Asian home. In contrast, the chinchilla, a rodent of the South American mountains which has particularly fine fur, was persecuted almost to extinction. At first sight a chinchilla looks like a small rabbit with a squirrel's tail. It is about ten inches long, has large eyes and long whiskers, and its tiny feet seem lost among the long, dense fur. Before the hunters and trappers set to work on them, chinchillas thrived in the Andes in Peru, Bolivia, Chile and Argentina, from sea level to 20,000 feet. Now the only wild survivors of the slaughter live high in the northern regions of Chile.

The decline of the chinchillas was sharp. Full-scale exploitation did not start until the 19th century and reached its peak in 1899, when half a million pelts were exported. Not surprisingly, the South American governments were alarmed at the near-disappearance of a valuable source of income, and first put restrictions on their export, then forbade their hunting. It was at about this point that some zoologists declared them extinct. The respective governments, however, proved them wrong by setting up small breeding establishments. In 1922 a nucleus of eleven chinchillas was taken to the

The Cuvier's mountain viscacha is often referred to as the mountain chinchilla. Related to the chinchilla it is becoming quite scarce due to being hunted for food and fur by local inhabitants.

Thousands of chinchillas were slaughtered for the soft, silver-grey fur. Just in time wild stocks were strictly protected and captive stocks now provide coats for women who wish to wear animal skins.

United States and proved, indirectly, the salvation of the wild stock. The breeding and sales management were so successful that chinchilla fur became comparatively common and therefore cheaper. It was no longer economical to hunt them.

The wild survivors live a communal life in the semi-arid upper slopes of the Chilean mountains. They are mainly nocturnal, but may be seen basking in the warmth of the morning and evening sun. There has been some doubt as to the number of species. Certainly, the animals of the comparatively lower levels have longer tails and ears than those of the peaks, and the babies of the higher levels undergo anything up to ten days more development before birth, but as has been noted, there is a tendency towards the reduction of body extremities and longer gestation times as the climate gets colder. It is

Opposite. 1. *Norwegian lemming, the source of legends about suicidal migration marches.* 2. *Antelope ground squirrel, from western America.* 3. *The hyrax, a small African rock-dweller.* 4. *Collared pika in winter.*

Overleaf. 1. *The buzzard's keen eyes and vicious hooked beak make it a formidable European mountain hunter.*
2. *Commonly found in the woodlands of Europe and North America, the goshawk also lives in the isolated Tibetan mountains.* 3. *A single, well-camouflaged lammergeier chick is raised in a rocky nest.* 4. *A lammergeier waits until vultures have finished at a carcase.*
Page 80. *African Cape vulture feeds on a dead zebra.*

1

3

2

4

1

more likely that, at most, the chinchilla has two races which can interbreed – true separate species cannot do this.

Food and water are scarce in the chinchillas' home. They eat coarse grasses and herbs, taking moisture from the plants and dew. The fur so coveted by traders is thick, and provides excellent insulation against the bitter cold of the heights. The babies are born furred and can run about a few hours after birth. If conditions become very severe they nestle between their parents, who squat side by side to form a furry nest. Thus by thick fur, spartan food requirements and long gestation, the chinchilla has found a niche in which it can survive.

Closely related to the chinchilla is the mountain viscacha; some authorities even refer to it as a 'mountain chinchilla'. The four species are found in the Andes and its foothills, to a height of 17,000 feet, from Peru and Bolivia southwards to the Argentine.

They are slightly larger than chinchillas, being about fifteen inches long. In the rest of their appearance they resemble chinchillas quite closely, although the fur is shorter and the legs appear longer. Mountain viscachas are social animals, living in groups of eighty or more. Unlike their nocturnal relatives, they are active by day, spending a lot of time basking in the sun, but feeding in the evening. By night they retreat to rock crevices or shelters in piles of boulders, where temperatures do not fall so low. Like all mountain rodents, they cannot indulge in a varied diet, because the range of plants is so restricted. Thus they live on grasses, moss and lichens growing round the colonies. The mountain viscacha bears only one young at a time and breeds three times a year. The offspring are hardy and nibble at plants as little as an hour after birth.

While they have not suffered the intensive and sophisticated hunting that nearly exterminated the chinchillas, there is some danger that mountain viscachas will become extinct in the near future. The main natural predator is the Andean fox, and the people of the mountains hunt viscachas for food and fur. They are sparsely distributed throughout their range and are becoming scarcer.

Short-tailed and long-tailed chinchillas were once believed to be separate species. Now it seems that chinchillas that live in the higher and colder regions have developed smaller ears and tails to prevent excessive heat loss.

Exclusive mouse, widespread voles

Although mountains form a unique habitat, there are only a few animals which are unique to them; most creatures of the highlands have very close relatives in the lowlands. There is, in fact, only one mammal completely peculiar to extreme elevations. The puna mouse lives exclusively in the Altiplano of Peru, between 14,250 and

The puna mouse's round shape and long fur help to retain the body heat.

16,500 feet. Although it looks like a normal, if rather chubby vole, this mouse has a curious anatomy. It is a short-legged, greyish-brown rodent, with long, loose fur. It is about six inches long overall, with the stubby tail taking up about a third of the length. The teeth are particularly interesting; the lower front teeth – incisors – are separated by a relatively large gap, and the surface structure of the grinding teeth is unusually complex.

Puna mice are quite common within their restricted range. Using the shelter of rocks, they are active during the day. They can have little competition for food. Their diet consists almost entirely of the two most foul-smelling plants encountered in this zone of the mountains, *Senecio adenophylloides*, a fleshy-leaved shrub and *Werneria digitata*, a herb. The mice cut twigs of up to two feet long which they manipulate into stores under rocks. Surprisingly, considering the apparently specialized dentition, the plants are not chewed very thoroughly. Like most mountain dwellers, the puna mice time their breeding to produce babies during the warm, wet season, when food is abundant.

Almost as exclusive in its range, but living at slightly lower altitudes, the Kenyan mountain shrew is an African parallel to this creature. Restricted to Mount Kenya and the Aberdares, between eight and ten thousand feet, it lives in the unique moss and giant heather cloud forests.

In general, voles have managed to exploit the upper slopes of mountains all over the world. In Europe, the snow vole has been the most successful. About seven inches long overall, with a two-inch white tail, it is a light-brown to grey rodent with long white whiskers. It lives in the mountains of Europe, in any part where the sun falls, reaching 13,000 feet in the Swiss and French Alps. Particularly in sunny weather, it appears during the day, running with tail held high and for its size, seeming very long-legged. It builds quite complicated but shallow systems of burrows with many entrances, and includes nest chambers and storage vaults in its home.

The nests consist of hay and stalks collected while feeding. The sort of pasture containing alpine roses is a favourite with these voles, where they feed on grass, shoots, bard and seeds. They are tame, familiar animals and show little of the customary animal fear of man. They will enter climbing huts in winter, sometimes even when the climbers are present.

Normally the vole's voice is heard as a shrill note, uttered at sporadic intervals. In the breeding season, however, from May to August, this becomes a continuous chatter. The four to seven young are born blind and helpless in the nest, after a gestation of four weeks, and join their parents on the lush summer pasture a few weeks later.

The quickest way up

He clasps the crag with hooked hands:
Close to the sun in lonely lands.
Ringed with the azure world, he stands.

The wrinkled sea beneath him crawls;
He watches from his mountain walls,
And like a thunderbolt he falls.

'The Eagle' by Alfred Lord Tennyson 1809-92

Lords of the air, the majestic birds of prey
seem to express the very spirit of the rugged
peaks and crags where they nest. They are
creatures of great beauty, flying and soaring
with effortless grace. Unlike the ravens and
vultures which share their home, many are
seriously threatened by man's activities.

In any walk of life, animal or human, complete mobility is an advantage. Nowhere is this more true than in the hunters of the mountains. Any creature on four legs is obstructed at every turn by snow, erratic winds carrying scent, and paws and claws less suitable for jumping around crags than for killing. Borne on the very winds that thwart their ground-bound equivalents, the birds of prey have twofold advantages in mountain life. Most are hounded by man, so they find safety in inaccessibility. Food is still available in the form of rodents of several kinds, such as voles, mice and lemmings. Those animals which succumb to the harsh life provide an extra food source for the bird predators. In the heights, most food is acceptable. When breeding, the more inaccessible the crag on which to nest, the more safe are their young.

Mountain bird par excellence, *a golden eagle soars for hours to patrol its home territory.*

Furthermore, bad weather merely dictates a drift to the lowlands.

The mountains are, to the birds of prey, however, more than just havens in which to rest; they are vantage points from which to survey vast territories. Some commute between high crag nests, habitual perches, and the lowlands surrounding them. They can hardly be termed true mountain dwellers, for their hunting grounds are the plains below, where there is abundant food.

The golden eagle, to Europeans a symbol of the mountains, must have lived by this method in an earlier stage of its evolution. Whether hounded there by persecution or by competition, it is now a true predator of the heights, and only where left alone will it take to sea cliffs and wooded uplands.

None but the least poetic or the most pedantic could fail to acknowledge this bird's title, 'the king of the birds'. If one accepts size as a criterion, this should be 'queen', for the female is the larger, at a wing span of 6½ feet, and body length of three feet. Both sexes are dark brown, with yellow plumage towards the head, and feathered legs. They live right across the northern hemisphere, occupying crags from Scotland, Norway and Spain to Japan and Kamchatka, the peninsula on Russia's north-eastern border. Each pair has its own hunting range, covering up to fifteen square miles. They are not as aggressive about territory as songbirds, but available food and some mutual repulsion serve to keep populations well spread out. In winter, when food becomes concentrated into pockets, the boundaries break down, and many hunt in the same area.

Masters of the mountains

Possible reasons for the widespread success of this bird of prey are its catholic diet and its ability to fast for days on end when game is scarce. It will eat anything that is flesh: small mammals from weasels to rabbits, birds, including ptarmigan and grouse (part of the reason for gamekeepers' persecution), snakes, sometimes fish and often carrion. Like many other raptors, it hunts by flying and swooping, or by dropping from a favourite vantage point. The long soaring flights associated with these eagles are not primarily concerned with hunting; the pair are patrolling their territory, advertising possession. In the breeding season, the male chases the female all over the sky, looping, swooping and circling. She, too, performs aerobatics, sometimes even turning on her back.

Natural selection is hard on the young of golden eagles. Two eggs are laid, one a few days before the other. Hatching, therefore, is staggered, and in the rough and tumble for food which follows, the stronger, usually the older, pecks, scratches and generally harasses the weaker. If food is abundant, then both will probably survive. If, however, food is scarce, then the rivalry becomes so acute that the weakling dies. This system has, apparently, a double advantage. Like most birds of prey, the golden eagle lays a high proportion of infertile eggs, so two are laid allowing for the one that often fails to hatch. If, however, both hatch in a time of plenty there will be two more eagles to continue the race. The fratricide occurs only in times of shortage, ensuring that the range does not become crowded, and prey over-exploited.

A bird as powerful as the golden eagle has few enemies, and the threat of overcrowding is alleviated by their behaviour. In recent years, however, they have suffered a sharp decline. This is directly related to the use of pesticides, particularly in sheep dips. The chemical dieldrin, eaten by the eagles with sheep carcasses, makes eggs infertile and possibly induces a destructive behaviour pattern, causing the birds to smash their own eggs. Since the use of dieldrin was restricted in 1966/7, breeding numbers have climbed back to normal. The golden eagle is not the only mountain bird of prey to suffer; the peregrine falcon's numbers have dropped sharply and in some areas are taking a long time to recover.

Other factors are involved; birds of prey, particularly large ones, are persecuted unmercifully wherever their range coincides with man's agricultural interests. They have been accused of every crime from baby-snatching to sheep-stealing. Lambs are certainly occasional victims, but there are no authenticated cases of eagles' carrying away human beings. Gamekeepers shoot anything with a hooked beak and talons, simply because it takes some of the birds – pheasants, partridges and grouse – that they breed. The birds of prey would be of far more use alive than as trophies on a pole. They take more than enough rabbits, small rodents, pigeons and other vermin to justify their position as friends of game protectors. Sport, too, plays its part. In North America golden eagles have even been chased by gunmen in aeroplanes. It is to

Left. *Despite its down-covered body this eight-day-old condor chick already displays the hooked beak of adult condors.*

Right. *Golden eagles build a huge eyrie to house the single chick which is carefully tended in the nest for ten weeks.*

the birds' everlasting credit that several of them have attacked and damaged the machines concerned. Smaller birds have no defence.

The golden eagle has an African counterpart. Verreaux's eagle, also known as the black eagle in South Africa, a black bird of prey, much the same size with white 'v' over the shoulders, occupies the same type of territory and behaves generally in the same manner. It lives on the high, boulder-strewn kopjes, on vertical cliffs and in the high valleys of Ethiopia and East Africa. Its main prey is the rock hyrax, and it occasionally takes hare, dik-dik and guinea fowl. It patrols the cliffs, relying on surprise to make a kill. The immobile instant of hyrax terror as this eagle sweeps unexpectedly from behind an outcrop is more than enough time for the terrible gripping talons to do their work. When not hunting, the eagles soar in the rising air currents, or rest for hours. Their territories are large – about 25 square miles. There are many other similarities with golden eagles, including the strife between chicks, although the usefulness of this seems expended. Hyraxes abound within easy hunting range, and less than a third of the available ones need be taken by the average family. The habit is, perhaps, an instinctive hangover from past times of overcrowding and hardship.

Scourge of the songbirds

Many birds of prey include the mountains in a much larger range and are not typical of them. The peregrine falcon, however, because of persecution, is gradually becoming predominantly an upland animal. It is a cosmopolitan bird, breeding in all the continents except South America and Antarctica. One of the larger falcons, it is

Above. *A peregrine falcon clasps its prey in its strong talons and rips off suitable-sized pieces for its young.*

Left. *A magnificent hunting bird, the peregrine falcon has been held in great esteem for centuries. When falconry was at its height in the English court none below the rank of earl might fly it.*

Right. *Gregarious Ruppell's griffon vultures squabble for the best position on a carcass. They nest in the mountains of northeast Africa but often descend to the plains for food.*

A present-day condor has a ten-foot wingspan but is overshadowed by the outline of its giant extinct relative Teratornis incredibilis.
Below. *The Old World vultures such as the griffon are the counterparts of the American condors although they do not quite match the condors' size.*

fifteen to nineteen inches long, with a wing span of up to 2½ feet in the female – she is the larger by about two inches length and six inches of wing span.

Although it is now, like so many birds of prey, suffering from human interference, the peregrine is one of the more successful species of hunting bird. The most obvious reason for this is its aerial prowess; few other birds can match this falcon's mastery of the air. Its whirling courtship chases, in which a pair twists, tumbles and loops all over the sky, are oddly matched by the speed and accuracy of its 'stoop' – the plummeting dive which culminates in a talon-torn back or decapitation for any prey up to the size of a goose. Estimates vary as to the speed reached in this stoop. One light aeroplane pilot, diving his machine at 170 m.p.h. was passed by a stooping peregrine 'as though the plane was standing still.' It is quite possible that it can reach 200 m.p.h. in a stoop from a considerable height. This superbly efficient method of killing prey accounts for the bird's prey list of over 120 species, all taken on the wing.

Another, more general, reason for the success is the bird's adaptability; it can nest nearly anywhere. Although nowadays its primary haunt is inaccessible cliffs, it has rested on heaths, moorlands and even in the middle of Montreal, Canada, four hundred feet above the sidewalk! The nest is merely a scrape in earth or booty from usurped ravens. The name 'peregrine' means wandering, and the falcon does cover a great deal of ground in search of suitable hunting grounds. It returns, however, to the same nest area year after year.

After the spectacular courtship the falcon lays three or four eggs all of which – at least in the absence of chemical poisoning – hatch. The male brings food to the female when she is incubating, then both feed the chicks as they grow. It is a measure of the peregrines supreme hunting efficiency that one male, after the loss of his mate, managed to feed three hungry offspring until they fledged.

Mountain peregrines move to the warmer plains as the weather degenerates, and often haunt the feeding grounds of wildfowl, or seek easy prey among the feral pigeons of towns. This migration is not habitual or instinctive; it is a reaction to diminished food. If the weather stays mild and prey does not move elsewhere the peregrine will not desert its nest area. Peregrine populations are spread out according to available food. They probably become aggressive around the borders of their territories if food becomes short.

In apparent contrast to the fast-moving birds of prey are the vultures. Most commonly seen soaring at great height on air currents created by heat – thermals. These scavengers take advantage of the height and inaccessibility of the mountains for roosting and nesting. All of them spend hours rising and drifting in the thermals, scanning the countryside high and low for the dead animals and offal which are their staple diet. The mountains present an obvious advantage to this type of life. If, by using up-currents and thermals, a vulture can assume a high perch before the air cools in the evening, it will have the advantage of altitude in the morning. It thereby expends little energy in reaching a height at which it can efficiently scout for food. Ground-living species have to wait for the earth to warm, then rise on the thermals.

The soaring scavengers

Vultures are divided by zoologists into Old and New World types. The most familiar and typical of the Old World species to use the mountains is the griffon vulture. It ranges from southern Europe and Northwest Africa through the Middle East to the Altai mountains of Mongolia, and northwest India. It has very close relatives of similar habits in South Africa and eastern Asia. It is a large bird, with a body length of forty inches and a wing span of about five feet. It lives in rocky, mountainous regions, descending regularly to the plains if food is available there. It is a gregarious bird; communal roosts

The lammergeier's elegant chin feathers have earned it the name of 'bearded vulture'.

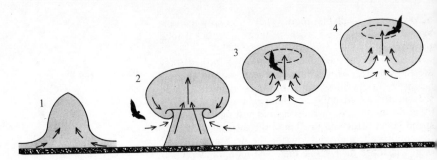

on cliffs are quite common. This high density has the advantage that many pairs of eyes seek the carcasses which are the main food. As soon as one vulture drops to feed, it is seen by another, and so on until all can join in a meal. Other birds and many ground mammals would soon deprive the griffons of a living if only one at a time were to feed on a large corpse. As it is, the birds gorge themselves to the point at which they can hardly take off. Griffons are not the most powerful of vultures. At a fresh carcass they have to wait for the stronger lappet-faced species to finish their meal before taking advantage of the breaks and cuts they have made in the skin to eat.

The vultures breed in holes and under overhangs of the cliffs, in colonies of five to fifty pairs. One egg is laid and when newly hatched the chick is comparatively small and feeble. The parents feed it by regurgitation and at about ten weeks its white coat of down is replaced by feathers. At this point the chick wanders around the colony, occasionally fighting with other chicks. It feeds from piles of regurgitated food left by the parents, which by this time are taking little interest in their offspring. As soon as it can fly, the chick is independent of them.

The griffon vulture is becoming rarer in Europe. Improved hygiene and direct persecution make regular inroads on its numbers, and there is little reason why the decline should not continue.

Also retreating from its former range is the lammergeier, the most handsome of vultures. It is often regarded as a link between the true vultures and the eagles and to complete the confusion, it looks like a monster falcon in flight. With long, pointed, swept-back wings and large lozenge-shaped tail, it contrasts sharply with the splay-winged look of other soaring birds. It is, however, one of the world's best gliders. In a shallow dive it can reach 80 m.p.h. and whether following ground contours at 50 feet or soaring as high as 25,000 feet, it scarcely has to beat its wings. The lammergeier lives from southern Europe to northern India, Tibet and China and parts of Africa. In parts it is very rare; there are, for instance, only twenty pairs left in Basutoland.

Much scorn has been heaped on the lammergeier for its 'cowardly' habits. The great naturalist Colonel

Like glider pilots vultures are expert at making use of thermals. A rising column of warm air (1) is undercut by cold air (2) and is forced upwards like a giant bubble. Vultures have learned to circle within these warm-air thermals to gain height rapidly (3 and 4).

Meinertzhagen said that it was 'ready to take advantage of any animal in distress, incapable of defending himself against creatures half his size and frightened at the wink of an eyelid'. One expects too much, perhaps, from this eagle-like creature. It is, after all, only a medium-sized vulture, and must wait its turn at a carcase, after more powerful birds like the griffon vulture.

The lammergeier is quite content to take leftovers; it has evolved both behaviour and digestion to deal with even the bones. The small bones it simply eats. A powerful digestive system copes with them. One bird killed in the Caucasus had the skull, legs and part of the horns of a chamois, the leg of a fox and the leg of a dove in its stomach. Larger bones are taken to a height of two or three hundred feet and carefully dropped onto rock. The lammergeier has a specially adapted tongue which gouges the marrow from them.

The nest site is usually on a precipitous cliff, often well hidden inside a cave. Only one young is reared from up to three eggs laid, so it appears that the survival mechanism of the eagles lingers on. After a few weeks of intensive feeding by the female, the chick is left alone with a supply of food. It fledges in about six weeks, and leaves the nest after three months. Its parents tend to stay in the nest area all year round.

Only two of the six New World vultures live in the mountains, but they rank as two of the world's most spectacular birds. They are the condors, vying for the position of the largest flying birds with only the wandering albatross, which has a larger wing-span. They are definitely the heaviest wild birds and have the largest wing areas. The wing span of the Andean condor sometimes exceeds ten feet, and a large male will weigh up to 25 pounds. Although spectacular it is dwarfed by the condors' extinct relative *Teratornis incredibilis* – the largest flying bird known – which had a seventeen-foot wing-span.

The Andean condor lives exclusively in that region, nesting and roosting at up to 15,000 feet. It sails and soars over the open savanna and occasionally frequents the Peruvian coast. Its food is exclusively carrion, spotted from a height – either directly or by the behaviour of other birds. Despite its size the condor makes no attempt to drive off eagles, coyotes or wolves. It waits, and feeds upon what they leave. The condors have naked necks and heads – adaptations for feeding inside carcasses without making the body plumage filthy. The general effect of this is to make the bird's head look like an old, fleshy-faced and ugly man.

The Andean condor is widely scattered around its thinly populated home and consequently has proved very difficult to study. Most of the information on its nesting comes from captive birds. The male's display is

Some species of vulture have plumage that is adapted so that feathers do not become matted while the bird feeds. The lappet-faced vulture (2) is a powerful species that can rip the toughest hide. This bald-headed species gorges itself on the outside of a juicy carcass. Once it is full other vultures such as the griffon (1) may eat. This vulture has no feathers on head or neck so it can delve inside the carcass to reach choice meat. The Egyptian vulture (3) is much smaller and by the time other vultures have eaten only a little meat remains. With no risk of becoming soiled by a carcass stripped nearly bare the head and neck of this vulture are fully feathered.

an upward stretch of the wings with curved and swollen neck. The normally red head becomes bright yellow, and the bird gives short 'tok' noises as it turns slowly around. They nest once every two years, either communally or alone, depending on the availability of suitable nest sites. They lay one egg, and tend the chick closely for a year. The combination of the bi-yearly mating and only one offspring tends to make the condors very susceptible to outside influence. The Andes are probably remote enough to protect the native condors; in California it is quite another story.

The California condor, essentially the same as the Andean, if a little smaller, is in danger of imminent extinction. Never a very common bird, it numbered only forty pairs at the last accurate census in 1964. In 1960, there were sixty pairs. The point has been reached at which only two young are raised successfully per year; three flying birds per year are lost to shooting and poisoning. It is protected by law, but unless a concentrated programme of education and law-enforcement takes place, the California condor will be extinct in about twenty years.

Peculiar parrots

Another unique bird of the mountains and alpine meadows which is facing extinction is the kakapo, an owl-parrot of New Zealand. A ground-living parrot, it

The male Andean condor presents a rather daunting sight with his bald head and huge purple-tinged wattle, which the female condor does not possess.

has many of the habits of an owl, and, apart from its predominantly green plumage, looks like one. It is large for a parrot, at 20–25 inches body length, and has soft plumage; it is incapable of true flight. It is unusual in that about a third of its body weight is taken up by a layer of fat underneath the skin. Owl-like, the kakapo has a disc of feathers on the face, an adaptation for sound collection and orientation. It also bears bristle-like extensions to the feathers at the base of the bill; possibly these serve the same purpose as the sensitive ones found on cats and other creatures of the night.

Although near-fossil remains indicate that its numbers were already dropping the kakapo was a very common bird in the middle of the eighteenth century. It is, for a number of reasons, very prone to interference. Introduced stoats take advantage of the fact that it has evolved in the absence of ground-living predators and have taken a fearfull toll. Introduced deer trample over the extensive patterns of pathways used by the kakapo to commute between nest sites and favourite dust baths. This ruins their social life, apparently essential to their well-being. The paths make fine scent trails for rats. Sleeping kakapo doubtless fall easy victim to all the introduced day-hunting pests. They are nocturnal, another owl-like habit.

Since 1958 the New Zealand Wildlife Service has mounted fifty-five expeditions into mountainous country in order to study and capture kakapo. It is tragic evidence of their decline that only eight have been found. Breeding rate is probably slow. Early reports, from the days when the birds were more common, suggest that it breeds once every two years, and that all the adult population bred in the same year. For a New Zealand bird, the kakapo lays its eggs late in the year, in January or February. This seems to be timed to produce the young at the season of

Opposite; top. *New Zealand's hardy mountain parrot, the kea, is a strong flier, often living high above the treeline but descending to forests at lower altitude in winter.*
Bottom. *Rare shot of the bald ibis; only 1,000 of these South African mountain birds are still in existence, and there are doubts as to whether the species will survive.*
Overleaf; top left. *Snow buntings nest among rocks and hummocks in highlands as far north as the Arctic.*
Bottom left. *Ever-hungry dunnock chicks stretch up their necks and beg for food. The bright red lining of the chick's mouth stimulates the parent to drop food in.*
Right. *The capercaillie, here performing his courtship display, lives high up in the pine forests of Europe's mountains, from Scotland to Russia and south to Spain.*
Page 100; top. *The red-headed, sparrow-like redpoll is a finch of woods and tundra.*
Bottom. *In fine spring plumage a cock willow ptarmigan struts out among the scrub on which it feeds.*

maximum berry and seed abundance. Adult kakapo feed on grasses, berries, and occasionally lizards. Like most parrots, they waste a lot more than they eat, leaving typical patches of snipped and carefully dissected grass.

Attempts have been made to isolate this unique bird on islands free of enemies, but the enemies have somehow followed; stoats swam to the Islands of Fiordland when 400 kakapo were installed on them at the turn of the century. It is heartening to know that the New Zealand Wildlife Service places it high on their list of priorities. If their past efforts with other animals are repeated, the kakapo may yet survive – just.

The kea is another parrot of the New Zealand mountains, but differs sharply from the kakapo in everything

Left. The kea is a large New Zealand parrot which has become a carrion-eater although its main food is still buds and shoots from the mountain forests of South Island. Here it uses its strong, curved beak to effect on a carcass.

Below. Unlike its garrulous parrot relative, the kapako is a shy bird, living a silent, nocturnal life in the forest undergrowth. It feeds on plants and small lizards, sleeping during the day under shelter.

except possibly colour. It is green, with lighter green underparts. With rounded wings and a span of over three feet, it looks very like a buzzard in silhouette. The beak is about two inches long, and not as sharply carved as in other parrots; it is immensely powerful. The name is derived from its cry. It lives on the mountains of South Island, on the border of the forests and the tumbled scree and boulder zone.

Keas are unusual in that they are not protected by law. Sheep farmers claim that they kill stock and whether this is true or not, the stories of their predations linger on. Bounties are still offered in some places for their beaks. They are normally bud- and shoot-eaters, taking some nectar with their brush-ended tongues. Since man brought sheep to their home they have taken to carrion, and it is easy to see a progression from this to attacks on live sheep. Judging by the parrot's behaviour when a victim flinches, it seems unlikely that it would persist with a healthy animal. Blood-poisoning from attempted attacks has been blamed, but there is still a remarkable lack of damaged skins to corroborate this. One must certainly look for other culprits when tales are told of farmers going bankrupt because of loss of stock. Like many birds they have learnt that man means rubbish and scraps, and tend to loiter around alpine huts and resorts, where they become quite tame. Although this tameness has led to many being trapped, and a large number are shot, the kea does not seem in dangerous decline. The introduced predators and rats usually fatal to ground-nesting birds

Opposite. *Pygmy owls are diminutive, often smaller than a starling, but they attack mice, small birds and insects with strength and speed – like a hawk. Pygmy owls are cosmopolitan, species being found in Eurasian and North and South American mountains.*

Left. *Although the glossy alpine chough is commonly thought of as a European bird it also nests in the High Atlas of Morocco and in the Himalayas.*

A raven's beak distinguishes it from other crows even in flight and at a distance.

Left. *The nestlings of an unusually light-coloured raven huddle in the shelter of a crag, a favourite nest site.*
Right. *A lone scavenger at the carcase of a deer. A bold and aggressive raven will drive other animals from the food.*

have made very little impression. Starvation after bad weather seems the primary cause of death. Through the winter they group in flocks of up to fifty, which have a fairly strict hierarchy; the weaker ones get least food and are eliminated. When the weather improves in spring, the flocks break up, and the birds go back to the upper levels.

They breed in spring and summer, with a peak of laying in October. The males have several mates in a season and may visit more than one nest. Incubation is the female's responsibility, and the male feeds her when she is sitting. The nests are hidden in a deep fissure or cranny in a crevice and three or four eggs are laid. Keas, like most parrots, are fairly long-lived; an adult bird ringed in 1956 was still alive in 1968. This, combined with an adequate rate of reproduction and the birds' resilience, seems to assure that the keas, if given a little protection, will continue to be unique and attractive residents of New Zealand mountains for many more years.

Alpine choughs soar for hours in the complex mountain winds.

Crows of the heights

Members of the crow family are the most intelligent and possibly the most adaptable birds in the world. Two of them, the alpine chough and the raven, are resident in mountains.

The alpine chough is a slim black bird with a yellow bill and red legs. It is usually seen 'playing with the wind' in large flocks, speeding up and down the intricate air currents around cliff faces. The alpine chough has a more low-dwelling relative the Cornish chough, which has a red bill and lives on cliffs in the lowlands and around the sea. The two ranges overlap in places, but the Cornish chough is on the decline, ousted by its cousin the jackdaw. The alpine chough is found in parts of the Alps, southern Italy, Sardinia, Sicily, Greece and extends across into southern Asia and China. It lives regularly at extreme altitudes. It breeds up to 19,000 feet and one was seen to land, and then with a long, awkward run-up, take off at 27,000 feet.

Insects and their larvae are the main prey, taken from the soft topsoil of alpine meadows by probing with the long beak, together with any other animal small enough to be manageable. They eat some plants. The choughs scavenge around rubbish dumps and will take carrion. As usual, there are. tales of sheep being attacked, but much the same arguments as those cited for the kea apply. After bad weather much domestic stock is lost, and the spectacle of a flock of choughs and ravens fighting over a carcase must raise the temper of any farmer.

Chough nests are built on high ledges, crags, and any derelict building that is high enough. They often nest colonially. The female does all the incubation and is fed by her mate. Once the chicks can fly, they accompany their parents to the feeding grounds and learn to fend for themselves. In winter, the alpine choughs descend to somewhat lower levels, even into towns, but are seldom seen in the lowlands.

In contrast to this specialized bird, the raven is completely adaptable and cosmopolitan, probably second only to the peregrine falcon in its success. It ranges from the northern tundra to the tropics of the northern hemisphere. It is all-black, about 25 inches long, and has a wedge-shaped tail and a hideously powerful-looking beak. Despite its apparent wide distribution, the raven is predominantly a bird of the uplands. It has nested up to 14,700 feet, living in pairs or small groups, but associating with crowds of up to a hundred. Like most members of the family it takes great delight in seemingly aimless gliding and soaring.

Part of the raven's distribution must be due to its wide diet; it will scavenge anything, especially corpses; it will kill weak lambs and small mammals such as hedgehogs, rats, mice and moles. In fact, it will eat almost anything, and is powerful enough to drive some other scavengers off the food. Like many members of the crow family, it buries surplus food, including seeds. This must serve a valuable function in the distribution of some trees, for many of the stores are forgotten, and the seeds may germinate.

Raven courtship consists of spectacular aerobatics and 'kissing' with the bills. Both birds build a large, very solid nest of sticks lined with any soft material available. Both parents feed the young, but they roost away from them: this has led to many legends of cruelty – quite unfounded. Numbers have been severely reduced; the raven is indubitably a pest on game reserves, where it takes eggs and chicks and has paid the penalty. It is unlikely that such an adaptable bird will ever be in any danger, particularly if, like many other persecuted animals, it can adapt enough to take refuge in the inaccessible heights.

Dippers, dunnocks and ducks

And range the world, and charm together
Birds of every note and feather,
And lead that varied troop as one
Into some safe and secret dell

'A prayer for the birds' by Edmund Blunden

Mountain streams and forests are the popular
haunt of a host of small birds, from dippers to
the adaptable finches. The dipper is an expert
at scurrying through the fast-flowing water of
streams and waterfalls in search of insect food,
while the wall creeper hunts on the steep rock
faces near the snow line.

Small birds are only too easily taken for granted. Wherever one goes, in city, cultivated land or wilderness, there is always some small, often dull-coloured 'sparrow' flitting ahead or away. If not seen, they are heard, as pipings and chirrups from cover, or occasionally as quite melodic song. Although by no means as common in the mountains, the smaller birds, together with the game birds, are well-represented. They have the same advantage – mobility – as the birds of prey, and there is abundant insect life for food. It is less easy to see why lowland species have invaded the lands of thin air and cold, when apparently better alternatives lay where they were already.

The game birds were probably forced there by the extreme climatic conditions during the great ice age – a period when the huge glaciers of the poles and mountains crept outwards towards the equator. They did this four times, between a million and ten thousand years ago, pushing wildlife before them or forcing it to adapt. Those animals which had previously lived round the poles were driven before the ice, and, as has been shown, there is little difference between the upper zones of mountains and the conditions which are home to birds like capercaillies, grouse and ptarmigan. Although all these birds are quite common in the mountains of the world, they are truly animals of the northern forests and the tundra.

More familiar evolutionary reasons are responsible for the distribution of many of the birds' homes. If they were hardy and adaptable enough to eke a living from the inhospitable heights, they then found little competition for living space, and gradually their form and behaviour became specialized to fit more perfectly. The ice age did, however, affect them. Some populations stayed where they had been driven; there is a breeding colony of choughs in the Simien mountains of northwest Ethiopia, nearly 1,500 miles from the borders of the main chough population.

The ring ouzel is another example. It was probably, in the distant past, an exclusively upper mountain bird, but with the enormous extension of mountain glaciers in the ice age it was forced to lower levels, well below the glacier line. When the ice retreated and vegetation started to creep back to the zones that exist today, the ring ouzel was well-accustomed to living in the stunted woods and tundra which had been features of the ice age lowlands, and did not always move back to the extreme heights. The belt of its occupation had, however, been widened considerably, and the northern European part of the population now lives on heath and moorland, around the rocky coasts, and on barren islands.

The low water mark of the ring ouzel's tidal retreat could not have crept any farther down the mountainsides without competition from its very close relative, the

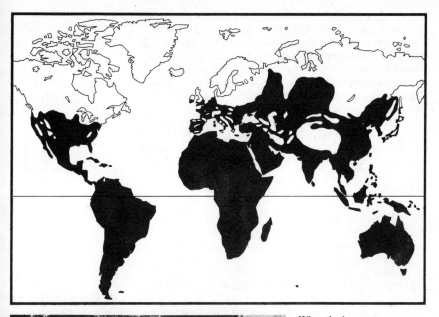

When the ice came

In the last ice age to affect the northern hemisphere, about 10,000 years ago, the whole of the area shown in white was covered with ice, and much of the land to the south was very much colder than it is now. Isolated areas of high ground were also glaciated. This has influenced the distribution of many birds. Polar species moved south with the advancing ice and when the ice retreated colonies were left behind in mountainous regions, where the climate was similar to that of their original home.

Mountain species, driven to lower levels by the extension of glaciers, did not always return to the heights after the ice's withdrawal. The ring ouzel (left) became split into two populations, one of which followed the tundra of northern Europe, while the other spread back up the mountains of alpine vegetation of southern Europe.

blackbird, resulting. The male ouzel is identical to the blackbird, apart from a crescent of white high on its chest and paler edgings to the wings. The female is brown, with a duller chest mark. The ouzel now lives in woods below the tree line and in areas of stunted and dead wood nest above the tree line. In addition it occupies alpine meadows on steep slopes with scattered boulders, preferably near mountain streams with grassy banks liable to flooding. It is distributed in all the high mountain areas of Europe, across Turkey, to just past the Caspian Sea.

Blackbirds, thrushes and sparrows

The ring ouzel resembles the blackbird in behaviour and habits, although it shuns cultivated ground of any kind in the breeding season. At other times it shows little fear of humans and will sing from a tree or bush undisturbed by passers-by. In flight it is more direct and less undulating than a blackbird, but landing is still accompanied by the characteristic flip of the tail.

The nest is concealed in a coniferous tree, and, like a blackbird's, is an open cup made of interwoven sticks. The northern European population usually build their nests on the ground, in rock clefts, or in the shelter of heather or juniper bushes. Both males and females build the nest and there are two broods of about four eggs. The parents also co-operate in feeding the young for two

Left. *The alpine accentor, a bird of mountain ranges from Spain to Japan, is a larger, more colourful version of the so-called hedge sparrow. It has a whitish bib with black spots and the feathers on the sides of the body are chestnut bordered with white.*

Right. *Another bird which at first sight looks a bit like a sparrow is the pine siskin, a North American representative of the finch family. In fact the plumage of this frequenter of pinewoods is distinguished from that of drabber birds by the greater amount of yellow.*

weeks. The ouzels probably have much the same diet as blackbirds: in the summer, worms and insects; in the winter, berries and the juicy fruits of trees and bushes. In winter the ring ouzels migrate to the mountain tops of the Saharan Atlas, where ridges and peaks are covered with light scrub interspersed with patches of open ground.

Closely related to the ouzels are the rock thrushes, which live on the warm, sunny slopes of the highlands from Spain to Japan, with some species in other parts of Africa and Asia. The bird bearing the species name, the rock thrush, is typical of the mountain members of this group. About seven inches long, the male has a pale slate-blue head, neck and shoulders, with a white lower back and a chestnut tail. The female has strongly brown-mottled upperparts, with mottled blue beneath. In winter the male's plumage tends to be obscured by buff fringes. It lives from the rocks and boulders of the arid lowlands to bare rock with scant vegetation above the tree line. The rock thrush shows a marked preference for rocky country. Indeed, the only sight one is likely to catch of it is a flash of colour with a loosely swinging tail, as the bird dives out of sight behind the nearest boulder. In the Alps and Caucasus it lives up to 7,300 feet, in the High Atlas of Morocco up to 9,600 feet, reaching its ceiling in Afghanistan at 11,500 feet.

Predominantly a bird of the ground, the rock thrush feeds on large insects such as grasshoppers and beetles; it will take caterpillars, and eats spiders, centipedes, earthworms, snails, and small lizards when they are available. Rather like a miniature bird of prey, the thrush sits on a high rock and swoops upon its quarry, consuming it on the ground. It builds a small nest in a rock cleft or among and under stones and rocks. It is migratory, moving to the warmer climates of the savannas, steppes and mountains of tropical Africa in the winter.

If the ouzels are the blackbirds of the mountains, then by appearance if not by scientific classification the accentors must be the sparrows. There are twelve species of these small brown birds, of which two use the mountains as their home. These are the Himalayan and the alpine accentors. The others live in the scrub vegetation and the woods of the lower levels; one is the familiar hedge-sparrow, or dunnock.

Height is no object to these two mountain accentors; they frequent the barren rocks above the tree line, and often venture onto the snow. The highest recorded nest was at 18,500 feet, and the Himalayan species breeds regularly at sixteen to seventeen thousand feet. Both are very hardy, and many remain in the heights throughout the rigours of winter, but young birds migrate to the forests of the foothills at the onset of bad weather.

Accentors are ground feeders, scuttling about with their bodies held horizontally, looking like mice as they search

The beaks of finches are stout and conical, and well adapted for cracking open seeds. The most specialised of all is the crossbill, with sharply-pointed mandibles which cross over and are particularly suited to extracting seeds from cones.

citril finch

redpoll

twite

crossbill

Perched among lichen-covered branches is a delicate citril finch (top), *a native of the spruce and larch forests of continental Europe, while nearer to the ground a twite tends its young in a nest in moorland scrub* (bottom).

for insects in summer and berries and seeds in the winter. Their gizzards are adapted for dealing with hard seeds; they have powerful muscles in them, and swallow grit to help break up the food. When not actively feeding, they move with leisurely hops, often giving a little flick of the wings. They do this a great deal when courting, and the habit has earned them the alternative name of shuffle-wing.

Most members of the accentor family gather in flocks, but the mountain accentors tend to be solitary, coming together only to breed. The male attracts a female by short, lark-like song flights and by twittering from a boulder or shrub. The male takes little part in nest-building or the incubation of the four or five eggs. He does, however, help to feed the young. Fledgling alpine accentors sometimes leave the nest before they can fly.

This dainty dipper, poised mid-stream with a beakful of food for its young, is an agile hunter in the rushing waters of mountain streams. It can completely submerge and 'walk' on the bottom of a frigid turbulent stream.

An underwater aviator

Some of the birds mentioned have modified their behaviour to life in the mountains, but none can equal the dipper. There are four very similar species of this starling-sized, wren-like bird, all of which behave in much the same extraordinary manner. Not only do they feed in mountain streams, but they are able to 'walk' on the bottom, completely submerged, and pick up their food. At a glance, the bird does not seem specially adapted for this. On close inspection, however, one finds very thick, soft plumage with extremely large oil glands at the bases of the feathers and nostrils that can be closed by flaps of skin. The family ranges from western North America and Canada (North American dipper) to the northern half of the Andes (white capped dipper), with breaks only in the region where suitable streams are absent. In the Old World it ranges right across northern Europe including all of the United Kingdom except southeast and east England and down into parts of Asia (common dipper), reaching Tibet, western China and Japan (brown dipper). In parts of Asia, the ranges of the latter two overlap, but there is little competition as the brown dipper tends to hunt in lower streams, and prefers to wade rather than dive. The brown dipper lives up to 6,000 feet, the common dipper reaches 16,000 feet.

Because the habits of all the species are basically similar, the behaviour of the common dipper will serve as an example. The bird flits from stone to stone over a fast, clear stream, bobbing the body in the manner that gave rise to its name. It then wades into the water or dives to search for food. Although appearing to walk along the bottom of the stream, it is in fact flying under-water, flapping its wings to keep submerged. It turns over

the gravel in search of caddis or dragonfly larvae, worms or freshwater mussels. The dipper is a pest in trout streams and hatcheries as it eats any eggs the fish have failed to bury properly. Its control of movement even in the swift streams is remarkable, but no satisfactory explanation of the mechanism has been offered. The dipper can also fly into or out of the water without regulating its speed. It usually stays under for about ten seconds in 12–18 inches of water, but is capable of a half-minute dive, reaching 20 feet. .

Once coupled the birds are very possessive about their part of the river, and drive away any intruders on their 5–8 hundred-yard stretch. They both build a wren-like domed nest under an overhang or in a niche facing the water. The female broods alone, leaving the nest only to feed.

Some dippers migrate to lower levels in winter, others stay on and hunt through holes in the ice. There is a slight southern movement of common dippers, probably youngsters, in the winter.

A community of finches

Perhaps less spectacular than the dipper, but adapted perfectly to a diet of the hard seeds of cone-bearing trees, the stones of fruits and the hard pods of ground plants, the finches have populated the mountains with great success. All of them are small, around four or five inches long, and are sometimes very brightly coloured. Their primary adaptation is of the beak; all the mountain finches have deep, conical beaks with tweezer-like tips, with which they can dissect cones for the seeds or tear apart the

Opposite. *A green plumed rifleman finds insect food by probing the bark of trees with its needle-like beak. Each tree is systematically searched, the little New Zealand wren starts at the base and spirals its way up the trunk before gliding down to start on the next tree.*
Overleaf; above. *The fast-flowing Andean streams have their own waterbird, the torrent duck. Its slender body and stiff tail help it to swim in strong currents with only the head remaining above the surface. The duck is rarely seen to fly, and spends its time perched midstream on a boulder, diving into the cold torrent from time to time in search of small water animals such as caddis fly larvae, snails and small fish.*
Below. *Harrassed dunnock parent deals with demanding nestlings. Commonly known as hedge sparrows in the British Isles, dunnocks are really mountain birds but became adapted to life in the hedgerows because of the absence of montane vegetation.*

heads of ground plants. The muscles closing the beak are capable of generating massive crushing power; it has been estimated at over 150 pounds per square inch in some species. One of the finches is, according to some authorities, the songbird that holds the record for regular high nesting; the rose-breasted rose finch breeds well above the tree line, quite often above 18,000 feet.

The citril finch, siskin, redpoll and twite are the northern mountain representatives of this universally successful group. The citril finch is perhaps the most interesting, for it is the only mountain bird that lives exclusively in Europe although it rarely reaches Britain; all the others spread into the middle Asian ranges. Both sexes are yellowish-green with a clear green wing bar. The bird lives in the spruce and larch forests, near to their upper border, often in company with other mountain finches. The citril finch is not as agile as its neighbours, being unable to hang from pine cones or to clamber up plant stems, but it feeds quite adequately on seeds prised from fallen cones, other seeds around the edges of the forests, or by tearing apart the flower heads of dandelions, hawkweeds and thistles.

It builds a saucer-shaped nest in spring, far out on a fir branch, and lays four to six eggs. Its migrations are limited. Winter forces the finch to below 5,000 feet, and it takes to the sheltered valleys where it is often seen with redpolls and siskins.

The redpoll has the largest range of all the mountain finches; it spreads completely across the cold/temperate belt of the northern hemisphere. It is a lightly streaked grey-brown bird, with a red cap of feathers on the crown. In feeding habits it is intermediate between siskin and citril finches. Like the former, it can clamber all over hanging cones or lean from the thinnest twigs with remarkable agility, also running up the stems of plants. Like the latter it spends a lot of time foraging on the ground. In summer it is not averse to feeding on insects,

Bare rocky slopes are favoured by the rock thrush at breeding time, and the nest is usually built in a crevice or in the shelter of a rock. The task of nest-building is performed by the female, a much less brightly-coloured bird than her blue and chestnut mate.

which it also gives to its young. It is a social bird and usually nests in small colonies, quite close to the ground in bushes or in trees. It has no regular or directed migration, but mass dispersal is quite frequent. When food becomes very scarce, great flocks of redpolls, often with siskins, leave their home ground and wander at random seeking better pastures. The birds seldom leave the temperate zone.

The siskin is a yellow-green finch, distinguished from the others by a yellow rump and yellow wing bars. Male and female carry the same colours, but the male is the brighter. It is primarily a forager in the trees, and does not hunt on the ground. It has a North American equivalent, the pine siskin, which resembles it in colour and behaviour to a great degree. The siskin's most interesting divergence from the habits of its relatives is that it moves about more. It has no regular migration, but nomadic flocks wander round in the winter, stopping in districts where food is plentiful, often staying in them to breed in the spring. It is sparsely distributed around Scotland and Ireland in summer, but is a common winter visitor to all suitable parts of the United Kingdom.

These three finches demonstrate an interesting aspect of segregation within a given set of circumstance and food supply. At first sight one would expect competition; they appear to be feeding on the same kind of food and trying to make their nests in the same forest zone. Closer inspection reveals that there are two completely different methods of feeding: agility in the trees and foraging on the ground. So the siskin, using the former method, does not compete with the citril finch. The redpoll uses a little of both, and has a wider choice of diet (and, not surprisingly, the largest range). There is also no competition for nest space; the siskin hides its nest at the very tip of a high fir branch, the citril finch nests a little lower, and the redpoll nests in the lower bushes and branches. Thus during the most critical time, the breeding season, the birds are separated twice over. In winter, when all face hardship and the instincts of spring have died down, they find common ground and move together.

Another interesting example of segregation within the finch family is that between the linnet and the twite. The linnet is a bird of the lowlands and meadows, the twite is its closest relative and ranges up to the extreme heights. The twite's main population is in the cold steppes and mountains of central Asia, but it has populations in Norway and northern Britain. It was one of the birds spread by the last advance of the glacial ice, which extended its harsh home conditions, then left the birds in pockets as it retreated. The two birds seem interchangeable: they eat much the same food, although a twite spends more time on the ground; the nests are nearly identical, although the twite sometimes takes to crevices

Removing the droppings of the young is one of the parental duties performed by redpolls as by many other songbirds. Like the ring ouzel, the redpoll frequents two types of country in Europe – the northern forest zone and the sub-alpine larch and cedar woods up to the tree line in the Alps and Carpathians.

in the ground instead of bushes; and the birds' behaviour at various times of the year is very similar. The factor which separates them is not known, but on the other hand direct competition and aggression between the two has not yet been observed.

The twite is probably the dullest coloured of the group, being brown with a vertically brown-marked light chest. It lives around ten to fourteen thousand feet in Asia, and tends to stay near to human settlement and agriculture.

In Europe it frequents the mountains and moorlands. It feeds on all sorts of short grasses by scurrying about and upon the seeds of taller plants by running up the stem. It does not seem to migrate, though nomadic movements within its range are possible.

The cliff-hangers

Like the finches which by specialization have conquered both high- and lowlands, the nuthatches have, by their ability to climb vertical faces and treetrunks, spread all over the world. The common nuthatch is the most widespread. It lives in woods, occasionally up mountains, in a wide belt across Europe and Asia. Its American counterparts, the white-breasted and red-breasted species, are

Just like sparrows, flocks of snow finches will feed on any scraps of grain or crumbs left by man, but their natural diet consists of insects and the seeds of alpine plants. The range of this sociable bird of bare rocky slopes and screes above the snow line is from the Pyrenees to the Himalayas.

familiar birds of forest, park and garden. There are over thirty species of nuthatches, mainly wood-dwellers nesting in holes in trees. The largest member of the family, the giant nuthatch from the mountains of central Burma and Thailand is about ten inches long, but this size is exceptional. The normal length is four to seven inches. All of them have long, sturdy claws and climb by a diagonal movement, resting on the bottom foot and pulling up with the top. Their beaks are long and sharp, and the predominant colour scheme is blue-grey above, with white, grey, reddish brown or chestnut underparts. Many of them have a black stripe through the eye. An exception to both colour and movement rules is the wall creeper, one of the most beautiful birds of the mountains, which is distributed in patches from Spain, across the Middle East to the Himalayas. About seven inches long, it has a charcoal-grey body, and brilliant crimson patches edging the black wings. There are large white spots on the borders of wings and tail. The tail is short, the beak long, slim and curved downwards. It hunts not by creeping up and down faces like its relatives, but progresses upwards by short, butterfly-like bursts of flight. It hunts on the humid north or east faces of rock, away from the sun, seeking spiders, centipedes and insects. This choice of diet is the same as that of the other mountain nuthatches.

The wall creeper shows a marked preference for inaccessible homes. It lives on steep and overhanging walls of rock with cracks and crevices, often near glaciers and just below the snow line. It ranges from three to sixteen thousand feet, but this depends, as with all other mountain birds, on the availability of its requirements at any level.

By living in the darker, higher parts, the wall creeper takes over from the rock creeper, a more typical nuthatch, which inhabits the lower levels in many parts of their range, and prefers the warmer, more sunny slopes. All the nuthatches nest in holes or clefts, with the nest and young well-hidden. They migrate to the lower levels for winter, and wall creepers have even been seen in towns.

Many bird families have mountain representatives, and it is not surprising that the swallows have used their supreme flying ability in at least one instance. This is the crag martin, a bird often found in association with nuthatches and sharing their kind of home in the mountain belt across Europe and Asia. It is adaptable and also lives in the lowlands of Africa. It gathers in small colonies, making a neat, typically swallow family mud nest in an inaccessible crack or under an overhang. In the lowlands it will use the walls of houses and has occasionally been seen to nest with sand martins. It feeds on the wing, taking insects within inches of the sunlit rock faces. It seldom wanders far from one spot and its plummeting aerobatics around the cliffs of its home are spectacular in the extreme. Migration for the crag martin depends on conditions. Some of the birds move to the arid belts just north of the equator as winter arrives, others merely seek the nearest sheltered place, and stay there unless conditions become too severe.

A hardy duck

There are many more examples of highland members of lowland families, all taking very much the same pattern. One worthy of note is the torrent duck, which, as its name implies, lives in the fast streams and rivers of the mountains. There is only one species living in the water that flows down into the valleys of the Andes. It is about 17 inches long, and the male has a white head with black longitudinal stripes. The back is brown streaked with white, and the underparts are chestnut, verging on deep red. The female has a cinnamon red chin, throat and underparts, a greyish back streaked with black, and, like the male, has mallard-like white tips to the wings.

Not only do these ducks live in streams of fast water, but they prefer the boulder-strewn rapids and waterfalls for a home. In these conditions, most water birds would be instantly swept away, but the ducks swim up and down, keeping the body submerged and the head above water. Their usual method of feeding involves diving from a favourite rock, submerging for about fifteen seconds, then returning. Insect larvae, snails and small fish are taken, grubbed from the bottom by the duck's rubbery bill. The torrent duck seldom flies, and if it does, keeps to the course of the river. In the most rapid currents it patters over the surface with frantically-beating wings. Waterfalls are usually overcome by flight, but when alarmed the duck swims over the edge, then hides in the sheet of falling water at the bottom.

The density of torrent ducks is not high – about one per mile of water. The nests are hidden under the overhanging bank, or made in the abandoned burrow of some other water creature. The eggs making up the clutch of two to five are very large – at least half an inch bigger all round than those of a teal, a marshland duck of equivalent size. This is an adaptation of the torrent duck to hatching very advanced young, capable of dealing with its harsh home. An adaptation for steering is to be found in the adult's tail; it is long and stiff, being used as a rudder in the water and as a support when climbing up rocks.

The torrent duck is not the only member of its family to live in mountain streams. The blue duck of New Zealand does this, although occasionally it wanders into slower waters and estuaries. Unlike the shy torrent duck, it is very tame. This has made it easy quarry for hunters, and it is becoming very scarce.

Altitude no object

The tiniest living thing
That soars on feathered wing,
Or crawls among the long grass out of sight
Has just as good a right
To its appointed portion of delight
As any King.

from 'To What Purpose this Waste' by Christina Rossetti

Insects are found just about everywhere in the
world. Thousands of feet up in the snow they
and their relatives the spiders flourish in what
at first sight seems to be a complete absence of
food. At lower altitudes, the alpine meadows
are made bright with the fluttering wings of
scores of butterflies.

Over five hundred million years ago the ancestors of the insects, flightless creatures just beginning to breathe air, crawled from the sea to face their evolutionary equivalent of the garden of Eden. The land was carpeted in plants, but there were no other animals capable of competing with them for food, or even of eating them. By the time the fossil record becomes complete enough to be interpreted fully, the great forests, whose remains are now our coal and oil layers, covered the land. Here was the most abundant and exclusive food supply, in an obviously warm climate, that the world has ever known. There could have been little competition from the other animals to appear during this, the Carboniferous period of geological time. In fact, when the amphibians conquered the land, they probably found the same advantages. The frogs' ancestors also had the bonus that any insects unable to fly were possible meals. The product of this early evolutionary boost is a modern insect population of 700,000* species, with hundreds yet to be discovered. They are by far the most numerous and widespread group of animals in the world. For comparison, there are 4,500* species of mammals and 8,950* species of birds. It would be surprising if the insects had not learnt to live in the mountains by force of numbers alone but they have other advantages.

Air pressure means little or nothing to the ones that live on the ground and seems to have only a slight effect on the others. Most breathe through systems of branched tubes leading into the body from all over its surface, called tracheae. Some of the very primitive ones still use the method of their ancestors and breathe oxygen extracted from water. Obviously, they must stay in damp places to live. Temperatures in the heights are dealt with in two ways. Being cold-blooded creatures – unable to maintain a constant body heat – insects need warmth for activity. Conversely, they merely slow down when the weather becomes cold. Also, because of their size, they do not need a large piece of ground on which to live; their world can be the space between two boulders, perhaps even less. While the overall climate may appear harsh, small pockets of warmth and sunlight exist. They need not be hospitable for long; it takes very little feeding activity to keep most insects alive. In the meantime they can remain torpid. The only restrictions on insect life are extremes of cold – sufficient to freeze their body fluids – and the loss of water which results from the combination of low pressure and very high or low temperatures.

Even the snow line is ignored by some daddy longlegs (six-legged insects of the family Tipulidae, not to be

* Rothschild, A Classification of Living Animals: Longmans 1965.

Winged wanderers 1

1. Erebia ligea *is one of a group of Satyrid butterflies known as alpines which are distributed over both the New and Old World. Most of them are brown-coloured with spots.*

2 *(female) and* 3 *(male). The common blue butterfly is a widespread species in Europe, and often strays up mountains. The insects pictured here were found in forest high above Loch Ness in Scotland.*

4. *A yellow butterfly,* Colias palaeno, *of peat bogs and high moorland. The caterpillar feeds on crowberry, a plant typical of the moors.*

2

3

4

confused with the equally long-legged harvestmen, which are spider relatives). With black bodies to absorb the sun's heat, and long legs to keep this acquired heat from melting the snow, they run about well above the border between the exposed rocks and the snow. If hindered by anything, however, they die. The heat of their bodies melts the snow, and as they cool the insects are iced in.

The mountains, therefore, lose some of their aura of inhospitality as far as the insects are concerned. Much the same rules apply to the distantly related but superficially similar spiders. These, too, regard the mountains as just another home – up to a point.

Fluttering and soaring

The level at which insect life thins out drastically is around 16,000 feet. Below this it goes on as normal; not as abundantly, perhaps, as in the lowlands, but limited only by available food. As one climbs, the most striking and obvious occupants are the butterflies. Few people who have rambled in the mountains of the world can have failed to be impressed by the numbers of colourful specimens flitting about alpine meadows, or by the profusion of caterpillars on heather and shrubs at some times of year.

A spectacular example is the Apollo butterfly. It belongs to a group of about thirty species related to the swallowtails which ranges across the mountains of Europe, Asia and North America. Its highest member reaches 20,000 feet in the Himalayas. The Apollo is the European representative, and will serve as an example.

Although included in the same family as the swallowtail, the Apollo has no extensions on the hind wings. It is white, like most of its kind, and, again in similarity, has black spots on the tops of the wings and black-bordered red eye spots pupilled with white on their lower surfaces. Some of the group are yellow, and have blue eye spots as well. The common variety is replaced at higher altitudes by the alpine Apollo.

All Apollos are adapted for altitude. The body is hairy and obviously retains warmth, and is dark in colour, thus absorbing the sun's rays. The wings are proportionally larger than those of other butterflies, so exposing more area to the sun. They have, however, a much more unusual function. The Apollo butterflies soar on air currents with wings stiffly outstretched, rather than fluttering like the majority of their kindred.

The caterpillar of the common Apollo feeds on orpine, a kind of stonecrop. It is black, with red spots, and when fully grown spins a cocoon in which to pupate. Growth is

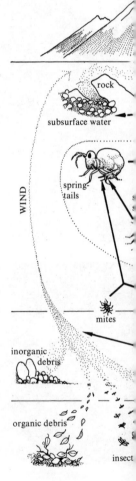

rock

subsurface water

spring-tails

WIND

mites

inorganic debris

organic debris

insect

Himalayan chains

Insects and spiders play an important part in the ecology of the high Himalayas. In this diagram, the creatures which live permanently above 19,500 feet are shown enclosed in a dotted line, while the other animals on the chart visit the heights only temporarily, like migrant geese and man

himself. Unbroken arrows show some of the direct relationships which exist between an animal and what it eats. For example, the droppings of birds such as the snow partridge form part of the diet of anthomyiid flies, while the eggs may be taken by weasels. Similarly, glacier fleas live on wind-blown debris and foxes and wolves on small mammals such as pikas. One special relationship exists between man and yak – man looks after the yak and takes in

return its milk and skins – while another concerns the scavenging birds such as the lammergeier and chough, which follow man and his domestic animals wherever they go. Indirect relation-ships are shown as broken arrows; for example melting snow collects as subsurface water in rock hollows where, together with rock-base soil, it provides a suitable habitat for lichens, fungi and flowering plants, which are the basis for most food chains.

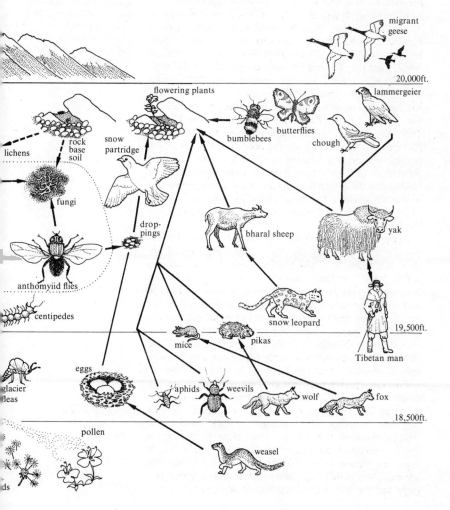

migrant geese

20,000ft.

flowering plants

lammergeier

butterflies

bumblebees

chough

lichens

rock base soil

snow partridge

fungi

drop-pings

bharal sheep

yak

anthomyiid flies

centipedes

snow leopard

19,500ft.

mice

pikas

Tibetan man

eggs

glacier fleas

aphids

weevils

wolf

fox

18,500ft.

pollen

weasel

129

slow, and completion of the life cycle takes two years. The early life of all the species is much the same, with the caterpillars feeding on stonecrops and saxifrages. The habit of spinning a cocoon, unusual among butterflies, is probably a preventative one; frost must be a great killer of the unprotected.

A butterfly family which extends not only up mountains but into the Arctic, the Satyridae makes itself familiar by its brown members, the wood nymphs and the meadow browns. In both the Old and the New Worlds it has groups known as alpines, chiefly dark brown butterflies with deep red patches or spots. Europe is particularly rich in them, and two of the species spread into western North America, southward in the Rockies, to Colorado. They live in all zones of the mountains and one reaches the Arctic. The true arctics live in even more rigorous conditions, and give a perfect example of the way in which the ice age glaciers distributed species, leaving them in isolated mountain pockets on their retreat, there to begin to develop along different lines to the original stock. First they formed sub-species, which look different but can still breed with one another, then full species which are not able to interbreed. The arctics have reached the sub-species stage above the timber line on the summits of the Presidential Range of New Hampshire, America and in the alpine meadow zone of Mount Katahdin, Maine. They are replaced in the Andes by a related species that behaves in much the same manner. Butterflies of this family cement their eggs to grass blades, and the caterpillars dig holes and cover themselves in silk to pupate. It is interesting to speculate on the place of this cold-defensive behaviour in the evolution of the cocoon.

Butterflies seldom inhabit any part of the world without the company of moths; the mountains are no exception. An example is the burnet moth. It is small and black, with five large, scarlet spots on the wings. It lives in colonies in the alpine meadow zone of Europe and on the mountain tops of Scotland. It flies by day and locally is very abundant; four or five may be seen on the same flower head. Adults feed on the nectar of flowers, sucking it up through their long, tubular tongues. If the temperature goes below a fairly high level they become torpid, but are protected from birds by their warning coloration. It advertises that they contain poison, in this case small doses of prussic acid (hydrogen cyanide) and any bird that has attempted to eat one moth will shun any more it meets. The caterpillar is dark green above and paler below. It has two velvety black stripes on the back interrupted by yellow spots. The head is black. Again in relation to its cold surroundings, it has a long life cycle – possibly four years. Little time is spent as a pupa and the adults live only two or three weeks.

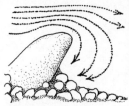

A feature of air movement important in mountain ecology is the dropping of wind-borne particles on the downwind side of rocks, where the air flow suddenly meets with decreased resistance. All kinds of organic debris, such as pollen and dead insects blown up from lower altitude, collect in rock hollows and provide food for springtails and others.

Two failed flies

On a much less ornamental level than the butterflies and moths, the small flies and midges live in the mountains as a matter of course, since dead animals, nests, rotting vegetation and fungus are to be found there. There are many of them, all quite well-adapted, but two families the mountain midges, stand apart as examples of evolutionary failure.

These two, looking quite similar, lay their eggs in the mountain rivers and streams, for much the same reasons as the hillstream fishes and torrent ducks live in them; they are an exclusive and, if properly adapted to, a very safe home. The larvae of both species are aquatic and have developed a bizzarre equipment of lobes and suckers with which to cling to stones. The adults, too, are alike, having many folds and creases in the wings.

Adults of the family Blepharoceridae catch and devour other insects in flight, while those of the family Deuterophlebiidae have reduced mouth parts and do not feed. The former have a world-wide distribution, but are confined to small areas; the latter live in the mountains of central Asia and North America. Their decline is due to the vulnerability and inefficiency of the larvae.

These larvae are able to survive only in water with a very high oxygen content, and so cling to rocks at such places as the lip of a waterfall or the sides of a pot-hole, where the water whirls and bubbles. The masses of food in the form of pieces of organic debris that are passed by the current must be ignored by the larvae; they are not equipped to reach or catch it. Instead they must content themselves with browsing on the sparse, microscopic growths covering the rocks. They must move about to do so, but to let go in attempt at quick movement would be to surrender to the current and instant destruction. The larvae therefore move sideways, releasing the three suckers on one side and putting them down firmly before releasing the three on the other. The pupa is found in the same place, but is permanently anchored to the rocks by three pairs of suction pads. If the water is shallow enough for the adult to reach the surface while holding on with its back legs when the time comes for emergence, the insect has the further problem of being swept away while its wings dry. Mortality at this stage is very high. It has been suggested that the net-like crinkles all over the wings of the adults are due to the indecent haste with which they have to take off – before they are fully dry, perhaps.

The overall effect of this precarious childhood is to limit the numbers of mountain midges. The black-flies and others readily take their place, being better adapted for it. A black-fly larva in a stream has only two suckers, and anchors itself by a thread of silk. It lives in the slower

131

water, where food is easier to catch, and when an adult emerges from its pupal case it has a bubble of air to breathe until it is swept into calm water, where it can take to the air.

At the weather's mercy

Up to about sixteen thousand feet, insects are fairly common considering the conditions; ants, bees, wasps, flies, butterflies, moths, beetles, bugs, hoppers, Mayflies and grasshoppers are only a few of the wide range that can be collected. Their behaviour patterns reflect the sudden changes that can come over their tiny worlds. At night, all flying insects seeks refuge in holes; in sunlight they are very active. In cloudy weather they become erratic. Bumblebees and flies crawl about on the ground or lie torpid. Butterflies lie helpless on their sides. It is at this point that the ground-hunting wolf spiders can hunt with ease. They are more resistant to cold than the insects they seek, and even appear, carrying prey, when snow is falling. Normally the spiders hunt at dusk, when the flying insects have taken to the comparatively warm earth to seek shelter for the night.

Wolf spiders, as their name implies, are hunters. Unlike many other spiders, they do not make webs, but run their prey down. They are small to medium sized, with bodies up to an inch long and a total span of up to three inches. Dark in colour, their bodies are covered in short hair or bristles. In keeping with their way of life they have very powerful jaws. Their most characteristic feature is the three rows of eyes on the head; four small

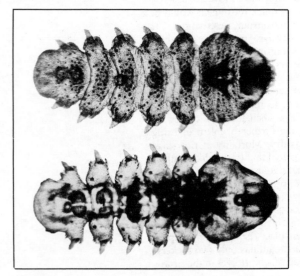

An assortment of lobes and suckers are the means by which the tiny aquatic larvae of the mountain midges cling to rocks in the strongest current. The upper surface (above) *and the lower surface* (below) *are shown magnified about 15 times.*

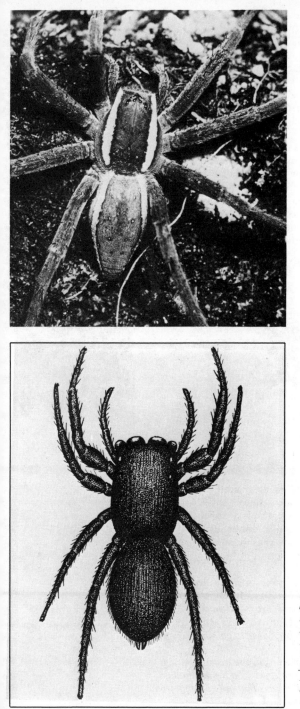

Proving that eight legs are better than two up mountains: a Thalassius *spider from the uplands of* Nepal (above), *and the immature salticid spider from 22,000 feet up* Everest (below) *whose discovery shed new light on mountain ecology.*

eyes in front, just above the base of the jaws, and two larger eyes in each of the succeeding rows.

The female, once mated, is devoted to the cocoon she spins around her eggs. She carries it with her, and should it drop off is retrieved immediately; should rain fall she will make for shelter and later hold it towards the sun to dry. This shows a marked contrast with her behaviour once the young have hatched. She carries the spiderlings, often several deep, on her back, and if one falls she ignores it.

The prey of these spiders includes a small insect rather like a housefly, which is in fact quite closely related. This is a fly of the family Anthomyiidae. Its lowland forms feed around birds' nests. In the mountains it eats fungus and rotting vegetation. This fly reaches great heights and was the basis for the discovery of one of the mountains' most interesting communities; the spiders and their prey that live above 18,000 feet.

Beetles and moths are among the many insects able to live without difficulty at fairly high altitude, like the beetle Dorcadion *(left), photographed in Spain's Sierra Nevada, and the Scotch or mountain burnet moth (below), whose range in Britain is limited to the Scottish Highlands at Braemar.*

The world's highest homes

That the spiders occurred at this level – indeed, at 22,000 feet – had been known since the 1924 Everest expedition collected some. Controversy about their way of life, none of it very positive, continued until 1954, when a team of mountain biologists found that they were preying on the anthomyiid flies.

Opposite. *Purple Pasque flowers in an alpine meadow attract a* Parnassius apollo *butterfly. Apollos are related to a group of swallowtails which are found on many mountain ranges. The furry body and wings retain heat as the apollo sits with outstretched wings to gain full benefit from the sun's rays.*
Overleaf. *This battery of eyes belongs to a wolf spider, a great hunter which manages to survive on the mountains by preying on helpless small insects that are swept up from lower altitudes in air currents.*

The spiders involved were the jumping spiders of the family Salticidae, whose distinguishing feature, apart from being able to jump short distances, is their enormously enlarged first pair of eyes. These probably serve in distance judgement, for these spiders hunt their prey by running and pouncing. When the sun is out, they prey on flies; when the sun goes in, they retreat to the darkness under rocks to prey on the residents there – crawling and jumping insects known as springtails.

Springtails are the most widespread of the primitive insects. There are about 2,000 species distributed all over the world. They have no wings, and fossil evidence denies that they ever had them. They are seldom more than a fifth of an inch long, and derive their name from a fork-shaped mechanism on their tails. It lies forward, underneath the animal, and is held with a 'catch'. When released, the fork strikes the ground and throws the springtail several inches into the air. Further evidence of their primitive makeup is their respiration; they have no breathing tubes and take in oxygen from water on the skin. Thus there exists at eighteen to twenty thousand feet a simple food chain, with jumping spiders at the top, springtails in the middle, and decayed plant matter and

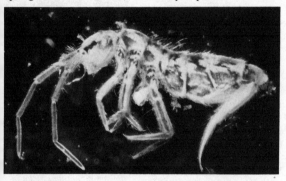

Top. *Poised to spring: the great jumping ability of the springtail lies in the flexed tail – when it is flicked back the animal leaps into the air.*

Bottom. *Springtails are not so insignificant that they escaped the notice of the 17th century monk who painted these quaint 'artist's impressions'.*

137

fungus at the bottom. The nearest approach to this by insect-like creatures is 19,300 feet by centipedes and a few mites.

In what is possibly the world's most inhospitable home a little lower down, some comparatively large insects have been found. The glacier fleas live in the ever-moving rubble of the glaciers at seventeen to nineteen thousand feet. They are very primitive insects of the order Thysanura, whose life is taken up with sunning themselves on rocks and feeding on wind-blown debris.

It is significant that the glacier fleas and the spring-tails, two very primitive insects, are the ones that survive in these desolate, lost places. Perhaps there is some analogy between this and the near-sterile land that faced their earliest ancestors (preceding the Carboniferous ones mentioned earlier) when they underwent the transition from sea to land. It is, perhaps this very lack of specialization which has made them so adaptable; many more advanced animals would be incapable of the simple adjustments these insects have made.

On the dry, rocky slopes above 18,000 feet, water is life's critical factor. Where water exists, plants, and insects, if only springtails, can survive. Small patches of plants are obvious on these slopes, existing on the water beneath stones. This water is made available by snowfall. The rocks protrude and, in contrast to the reflection of the white surrounding surface, absorb heat from the sun. Their acquired heat melts a little of the snow, preventing the usual evaporation without a liquid stage that occurs at reduced pressure. The water accumulates under the rock. This tiny niche has another advantage; the down-wind side is an efficient trap for the airborne organic debris, like dead insects and pollen. Mountain plants produce large quantities of pollen. The seeds, and insect young which use 'parachute' dispersal to rise on streams of filament, are carried by wind and thermals from the lower levels. Springtails generally turn up where there are plant or animal remains. Yet under barren rocks at 20,000 feet, with no visible indication of plants, some of them have been found. Their presence suggests that they live on microscopic wind-blown debris. If so, it is logical that they should live at even higher levels. Thus, beyond the alpine zone there may exist a community sustained by wind-borne debris alone. Temperature is not a great problem; a long active period would not be necessary. The sun heats rocks at high altitude more than lower ones; the air is thinner and absorbs less warmth. This of course works the other way, there is less air for insulation and the land becomes colder after dusk. Whatever the possibilities, the Everest spiders were certainly not frozen at 22,000 feet, and all evidence points to their being offspring of permanent residents.

The mayfly is an insect which spends most of its life as an immature water-dwelling nymph. This newly-emerged adult female, poised above a swift-flowing mountain stream in Scotland, has but a very brief time ahead of her in which to mate, lay her eggs and die.

Men, women and mountains

**Great things are done when men and mountains meet.
This is not done by jostling in the street**

'Epigrams' by William Blake 1757-1827

The conquest of Everest was a crowning human
achievement, but man has been conquering the
heights in less dramatic ways for centuries. His
body has become adapted to the new physical
demands and he has enlisted the aid of hardy
animals such as the llama and yak, which
provide food, transport and clothing.

So basic are the obstacles presented by mountains that even man has much the same problems as the animals. Obviously, the same conditions prevail: the terrain is difficult, sometimes even impossible; the temperature and the pressure lower with height; and the highlands are isolated from the rest of the world by the physical difficulty of travel. Man retains, however, his adaptability and the capacity to change nature to some extent to suit his ways. For him, the mountains' characters have changed with the ages. In prehistoric times the heights were almost insurmountable barriers, cutting off populations and limiting their spread. In the historical past they have become boundaries for territory, being easily defended from narrow passes. In modern times they have become pleasure and health resorts and retreats for the recluses of advanced civilization. Yet they still remain home to some advanced and some very backward communities.

The greatest obstacle presented to man is that of terrain. As well as expending energy in the sheer physical action of climbing and descending slopes, he must farm and build. These activities, too, are hampered. Neither his buildings nor his topsoil must be allowed to succumb to gravity and move down the mountainsides. The force of water released by heavy rain or thaw is often enough to do both. Topsoil is particularly vulnerable, for it cannot be replaced, and to farm it, one must break it up by ploughing or digging. This helps the erosion by wind, rain and thaw. The answer has been to build terraces; millions of people in Asia and India devote their entire lives to building and maintaining these. For them, there has been little time or energy left to advance their standards of living.

Left. *Domesticated yak are vital to the livelihood of the Himalayan peoples. As well as their main function as beasts of burden, they provide hides for clothing, and milk.*

Right. *The shaggy llama plays an equally indispensable role in the life of the Andes Indians. The wool, meat and fat are all put to good use and even the dung is burnt for fuel.*

Temperatures contrast sharply. In the temperate zone, the reduction related to height dictates that snow carpets the ground for two-thirds of the year; the farmer must keep hardy, independent animals like goats, and harvest what he can in the brief summer. In the hot zones the mountains are much more hospitable. At the intermediate heights the climate is warm, there is more than adequate rainfall on the windward side, and the area is free of lowland diseases like sleeping sickness and malaria, which are transmitted by insects of the hot plains and marshes. These conditions have fostered at least one great civilization: that of the Incas of the Andes. The limit on man's upward migration in these latitudes is set by pressure rather than temperature. Yet in the course of only a few hundred thousand years mountain man has adapted physically to the comparative lack of oxygen in the air.

Survival in the blood

Like all the higher animals man takes in oxygen and distributes it to the tissues via the blood. The transporters within the blood are the red corpuscles, which contain the carrier chemical, haemoglobin. It follows that if one has more blood and red corpuscles, then one can transport more oxygen. This is precisely what has happened in the men of the high mountains. An Andean Indian has a fifth more blood than his lowland counterpart, and consequently more corpuscles. Moreover, these contain two-thirds more haemoglobin and are comparatively large, giving a greater area over which

oxygen can be absorbed and carried. Because the blood is very thick, a consequence of this concentration, the heart has to work harder and is enlarged, again by about a fifth. Oxygen gets to the blood through the lungs, passed through tiny bags known as alveoli. Mountain people have larger lungs than lowlanders, and their alveoli are perpetually open. This added lung capacity gives them a characteristic stocky shape – corresponding with the short and stumpy appearance of the limbs; blood does not have to be pumped so far. The tiny tubes which connect arteries and veins in the stubby fingers and toes of these people are unusually large in number, and such is their efficiency that both the Sherpas of the Himalayas and the Indians of the Andes are able to walk across snow at fantastically low temperatures without the blood becoming thick and clotted, as it does in lowlanders, causing frostbite. But man needs more than these adaptations to survive in any numbers at great altitude; in the two greatest mountain ranges, the Andes and the Himalayas, he has been assisted by animals.

Essential animal companions

The Indians that now inhabit the Andes are a race descended from the sophisticated civilization of the Incas, and, as they did, depend greatly upon the llama, and its relatives the guanaco, vicuna and alpaca. The llama, like the men who keep it, has adaptations of the blood for living at great heights. Its haemoglobin is capable of carrying more oxygen than that of any other mammal, and the red corpuscles have the long life span of 235 days – as against 100 days in human blood. Although it baulks at loads of more than fifty pounds the llama is used for transport, and provides meat, wool for clothing, hides for sandals and fat for candles. If braided, the wool can be used to make rope. Even the dung is useful; when dried it becomes fuel for fire. The alpaca is a smaller relative of the llama, bred for the exceptionally fine quality of its wool. The vicuna and alpaca live wild and are virtually untameable. Good vicuna material commands up to £100 a yard in London and poaching was driving the population into a perilous position. The British government banned import of the skins in 1970, following the South American ban on the export of skins in the previous years. The United States allow only licensed skins – those with export permits from animals bred on government farms – to enter their shops. What difference these bans will make remains to be seen; there will always be poachers as long as outlets can be found.

The domestication of the llama and its relatives

Above. *The weatherbeaten face of a Nepalese Sherpa, one of the famous mountaineering porters whose expert knowledge and ability to carry loads of up to 250 lb. have contributed to the success of many climbs.*

Opposite. *Carefree interlude: this Peruvian boy is able to go about with hands and feet uncovered in spite of the cold, because of an improved blood circulation typical of Andean Indians. In the background can be seen terraces which continue a system of farming virtually unchanged since the Incas.*

143

stretches back 4,500 years, according to remains un-
earthed in settlements, but our knowledge of its biology
and origins is scant. This can be attributed in part to the
pessimistic assessment of South America sent back to
Europe when the Spaniards conquered the Incas in
1592. Whether this information was falsified to give an
impression of poverty to Spanish territory to reduce its
desirability to other powers or not, no adequate naturalist
was allowed into South America until towards the end of
the 18th century. The lost 200 years have never been
made up.

Tibet, too, has long been shrouded in mystery, but for
less imperial reasons. In the manner of so many animals,
the ancestors of the modern Tibetans sought sanctuary
in the remoteness and inaccessibility of the vast Himalayan
plateau. At an average altitude of 15,000 feet this is ringed
by the world's largest collection of great peaks. Not content
with this geographical isolation, the Tibetans used every
means at their disposal to keep out strangers. Their
capital city Lhasa, at 11,830 feet, eventually became
known as the 'forbidden city'. They managed to keep up
this isolation until the Chinese communists invaded in
1951. Like the Andeans, their society was dominated by
religion; before the invasion every third man was a
monk, and everything was dominated by the Dalai
Lama, or god-king.

The Tibetans depend even more than the Andeans
on one animal – a long-haired smaller and domesticated
version of the second largest buffalo in the world: the
yak. One cannot milk a llama, but the yak provides
milk, as well as meat, wool, butter and transport. Its
main function is as a beast of burden. An incredibly
hardy animal, the wild form has been seen at up to
20,000 feet, and in temperatures as low as $-40°C$.
The Tibetans herd the domestic forms from one sparse
pasture to the next, and the wild form has been steadily
edged into the highest and most inaccessible places. The
yak is truly the basic unit of Tibetan economy. Its butter
is used to pay taxes to the monasteries, and statues for
religious gatherings are made of it. The animals can be
crossed with oxen to give a creature known as a zo,
almost indistinguishable from normal domestic yak. It is
used to carry goods on the lower levels, while the pure
yak carries primarily in the extreme heights. Despite its
size and apparent bulkiness, it is far from being clumsy;
a yak can pick its way along the most precipitous of
paths with ease.

The inhabitants of the Himalayas are not the only
ones to have sought sanctuary in the mountains. Many
defeated and hunted peoples have 'taken to the hills'.
When the roving Moslem armies decimated North
Africa twelve centuries ago the Berber tribesmen
retreated to the heights of the Atlas range. As if further

Right. *An engraving by the
19th-century artist Gustave
Doré depicts one of the most
famous alpine accidents, in
which four members of
Edward Whymper's
Matterhorn expedition
plunged to their deaths.*

Below. *Techniques of rock
climbing are demonstrated
at a Swiss mountaineering
school. Unlike the mountain
goats, man is not a born
climber, and surefootedness
on the crags comes only
with practice.*

to prove its adaptability, the camel, usually regarded as 'the ship of the desert', is still their basic animal. Drought may have driven many plains dwellers to the lush valleys below rain-catching peaks. The Lebanon, a fairly fertile outpost, surrounded by arid lands seems an example. The people surrounding it are of a different religion, indicating that they moved in when the ancestors of the Lebanese made their ways to the hills.

Because they are there

Populations go to the mountains because they are driven there; because the climate suits their projected way of life; or simply because, reared in the area, they are too bound up in the serious business of fighting the surrounding conditions for a living that there seems no alternative. Their isolation works both ways. Few people communicate with the hard, independent and usually inhospitable people of the heights. Many of them are, therefore, out of touch. A Caucasian tribe called the Khevsurs were still wearing crusades-style armour until well into the 20th century. Men of the lowlands dislike crossing mountains, be they bent on travel, on invasion, or only on pilgrimage. They tend to go round, rather than over the heights. They maintained that mountains were 'nature's rejects': deviations from the 'Divine Plan', and would not even look upon them.

This changed in the mid-19th century, when British climbers first showed that peculiar attraction to the heights which seems typical of the Anglo-Saxons, and has done much to encourage mountaineering. Perhaps the most controversial climb of this period was made by Edward Whymper, a 26-year-old Englishman whose

Left. *A historic moment as Tenzing becomes 'the highest man on earth'. The summit of Everest was reached at 11.30 a.m. on May 29, 1953, the climax of a thirty-year battle to conquer the peak.*

Right. *Climbers on a ridge near the summit of the Eiger, one of Switzerland's famous peaks. For the adventurous the rewards of mountaineering are great. Above the clouds the cares of the world are left far below, and there are few other human achievements to match the exhilaration which comes from a difficult climb successfully completed.*

original connection with mountains was that he had been sent by a publisher to make sketches of them. With friends, he climbed the Matterhorn (14,685 feet) on his eighth attempt. The interest in this is two-fold. Firstly, the Matterhorn had proved very difficult and had repulsed many other attempts to climb it. Secondly, in a much more morbid vein, four men were lost in an accident on the way down, caused by a combination of one climber's incompetence and a rope that was too old to be safe. One of the dead was a local guide, and allegations of treachery and cowardice were to be thrown at Whymper and the other survivors for many years to come.

In the years that followed, expansion was the watchword. All over the world, mountains were found and conquered, although many men died in their attempts. It was not until the 1920s, however, that the world's highest, Everest (29,002 feet) was seriously challenged. Failure followed failure; the main enemy was the incredible fatigue and mental strain brought about by exertion at these tremendous heights. Men travelled, at times, at less than a snail's pace, and were forced back from within only 1,000 feet of the summit. On the British 1924 expedition, in the face of imminent monsoon, Mallory and Irvine made a desperate dash for the summit. When last seen they were 'going strong'. They were never seen again, and the only trace found has been an ice axe at 28,000 feet. Were they the first to the top? Only traces of them at the summit could confirm this, and no Everest expedition has yet found them.

Before Everest's conquest was to come another climb of almost suicidal audacity and incredible courage. In 1950, Maurice Herzog led a French team to the first ascent of an 8,000 metre peak: Annapurna (26,502 feet). He succeeded by making the final assault at ridiculous speed, but a series of accidents marred the occasion, and Herzog lost all his fingers and toes to frostbite, suffering the most excruciating agony on the weeks-long journey back across the Himalayan plateau. Everest was finally overcome by the British expedition of 1953. It was, perhaps, technological advance that took them to the top, as well as the courage of Edmund Hillary, the New Zealander, and Tenzing, the Sherpa, who were the victorious pair. Oxygen apparatus was by then light enough to be worth carrying, and reliable enough to last the climb. Unclimbed peaks still remain, and new routes up climbed ones are always there to be tried; mountaineers will always have an escape from the pressures of the crowded lowlands. They are taking, after a fashion, to the refuge that has sheltered exceptional people and animals for thousands of years. Unspoilt, as yet, by technology's intrusion, sheltered by conditions from the rest of the world, the mountains will prove outposts of sanity and preservation for many years to come.

Indexes

Numbers in italics indicate illustrations

Scientific names

Invertebrates

Vertebrates

AMPHIBIANS
Frogs order Salientia
  Hamilton's *Leiopelma*
  hamiltoni
Toads order Salientia

REPTILES
Two-lined chameleon *Chamaeleo*
  bitaeniatus

BIRDS
Accentor
  Alpine *Prunella collaris*
  Dunnock or Hedge sparrow
  Prunella modularis
  Himalayan *Prunella himalayana*
Augur buzzard *Buteo rufofuscus*
Bald ibis *Geronticus calvus*
Capercaillie genus *Tetrao*
Chough
  Alpine *Pyrrhocorax graculus*
  Cornish *Pyrrhocorax pyrrhocorax*
Condor
  Andean *Vultur gryphus*
  California *Gymnogyps*
  californianus
Crag martin *Ptyonoprogne*
  rupestris
Creeper
  Rock *Sitta tephronota*
  Wall *Tichodroma muraria*
Crossbill genus *Loxia*
Dipper
  Brown *Cinclus pallasii*
  Common *Cinclus cinclus*
  North American *Cinclus*
  mexicanus
  White capped *Cinclus*
  leucocephalus
Duck
  Blue *Hymenolaimus*
  malacorhynchos
  Torrent *Merganetta armata*
Eagle
  Golden *Aquila chrysaetos*
  Verreaux's *Aquila verreauxi*
Finch
  Citril *Serinus citrinella*
  Rose-breasted rose
  Carpodacus puniceus
  Snow genus *Montifringilla*
Goshawk family Accipitridae
Grouse family Tetraonidae
Kakapo *Strigops habroptilus*
Kea *Nestor notabilis*
Lammergeier *Gypaetus barbatus*
Lesser redpoll *Acanthis flammea*
Linnet *Acanthis cannabina*
Nuthatch
  Common *Sitta europaea*
  Giant *Sitta magna*
  Red-breasted *Sitta canadensis*
  White-breasted *Sitta*
  carolinensis
Owl
  Pygmy *Glaucidium passerinum*

Tengmalm's *Aegalius funereus*
Peregrine falcon *Falco peregrinus*
Raven *Corvus corax*
Rifleman *Acanthisitta chloris*
Ring ouzel *Turdus torquatus*
Rock thrush *Monticola saxatilis*
Siskin *Carduelis spinus*
  Pine *Carduelis pinus*
Snow bunting *Plectrophenax*
  nivalis
Snow partridge *Lerwa lerwa*
Swallow family Hirundinidae
Swift family Apodidae
Twite *Acanthis flavirostris*
Vulture
  Cape *Gyps coprotheres*
  Egyptian *Neophron percnopterus*
  Griffon *Gyps fulvus*
  Lappet-faced *Torgos*
  tracheliotus
  Ruppell's griffon *Gyps rueppellii*
Willow ptarmigan *Lagopus*
  lagopus

MAMMALS
Alpaca *Lama pacos*
Andean fox genus *Dusicyon*
Antelope ground squirrel
  Ammospermophilus harrisi
Bear
  American black *Euarctos*
  americanus
  Brown or Grizzly *Ursus arctos*
  Himalayan black *Selenarctos*
  thibetanus
  Spectacled *Tremarctos ornatus*
Bighorn *Ovis canadensis*
Caribou *Rangifer tarandus*
Cat-bear or Red panda *Ailurus*
  fulgens
Chamois *Rupicapra rupicapra*
Chinchilla *Chinchilla laniger*
Coyote *Canis latrans*
Field vole *Microtus agrestis*
Fisher *Martes pennanti*
Goat
  Bezoar *Capra aegagrus*
  Rocky Mountain *Oreamnos*
  americanus
  Wild *Capra hircus*
Goral
  Brown *Nemorhaedus baileyi*
  Grey *Nemorhaedus goral*
  Red *Nemorhaedus cranbrooki*
Guanaco *Lama huanacos*
Gundi *Ctenodactylus gundi*
Hare
  Alpine or Blue *Lepus timidus*
  Varying or Snowshoe *Lepus*
  americanus
Hyrax family Procaviidae
Ibex
  Alpine *Capra ibex*
  Siberian *Capra sibirica*
  Spanish *Capra pyrenaica*
  Walia *Capra walie*

Kenyan mountain shrew
  Surdisorex norae
Klipspringer *Oreotragus*
  oreotragus
Llama *Lama peruana*
Markhor *Capra falconeri*
Marmot
  Alpine *Marmota marmota*
  Yellow-bellied *Marmota*
  flaviventris
Mouflon
  Asiatic *Ovis orientalis*
  European *Ovis musimon*
Mountain viscacha *Lagidium*
  peruanum
Norwegian lemming *Lemmus*
  lemmus
Panda *Ailuropoda melanoleuca*
Pika genus *Ochotona*
Puma or Cougar or Mountain
  lion *Felis concolor*
Puna mouse *Punomys lemminus*
Rabbit *Oryctolagus cuniculus*
Serow genus *Capricornis*
Snow leopard *Uncia uncia*
Snow vole *Microtus nivalis*
Stoat *Mustela erminea*
Tahr genus *Hemitragus*
Takin *Budorcas taxicolor*
Timber wolf *Canis lupus*
Tur
  Darghestan *Capra caucasica*
  Kuban *Capra cylindricornis*
Vicuna *Lama vicugna*
Weasel *Mustela nivalis*
Wildcat *Felis sylvestris*
Wolverine *Gulo gulo*
Yak *Bos mutus*

151

For permission to use published/copyright material we would like to thank the following:

Gerald Duckworth & Co Ltd and Alfred A Knopf, Inc, for the poem *The Chamois* by Hilaire Belloc from the book 'Cautionary Verses'; The Lilian Bowes Lyon Estate and Jonathan Cape Ltd for an extract from *The White Hare* by Lilian Bowes Lyon, taken from 'The Animal Anthology', edited by Diana Spearman and published by John Baker; the author and Sidgwick & Jackson Ltd for an extract from the poem *A Prayer for the Birds* by Edmund Blunden, taken from 'The Animal Anthology'; Macmillan and Company Ltd for the poem *The Eagle* by Alfred Tennyson; also for an extract from *To What Purpose this Waste* by Christina Rossetti, taken from 'The Animal Anthology'.

Photo Credits

Cover – Dick Robinson: B Coleman
1 – Joe Van Wormer
2 – Ernst Heiniger
7 – Peter Hill
10T – Peter Hill
B – EO Hoppe
11TL, TR – Barnabys
B – Peter Hill
13 – Keystone
14T – MF Soper
B – Simon Trevor: B Coleman
15 – Eric Hosking
16 – AW Engman: B Coleman
17 – Russ Kinne: B Coleman
18 – John Tashjian at Steinhart Aquarium
19T – CJ Ott: B Coleman
B – Atlas
20 – Jane Burton: B Coleman
21 – T Angermayer
23 – MF Soper
25 – R Petocz
26T – Chris Sandy
C,B – R Petocz
27, 28, 29 – R Petocz
30 – Okapia
32 – Popperfoto
33 – Okapia
37T – F Vollmar: WWF
B – South African Tourist Corporation
38 – Philip Wayre: NHPA
39T – Des Bartlett: B Coleman
B – Jean-Philippe Varin: Jacana
40 – Dick Robinson: B Coleman
41 – Okapia
42T – E Lindsey
B – R Petocz
43TL,TR – Okapia
BL,BR – Rudolf Hofer
44,45 – W Röhdich
47 – Ernst Heiniger
49 – Sven Gillsäter: Tiofoto
50 – Okapia

51 – Joe Van Wormer
53T – Peking Zoo: WWF
B – London Express & News Features
54T – Associated Press
B – Eric Shipton: Mount Everest Foundation
55TL – Don Whillans
TR – Eric Shipton: Mount Everest Foundation
BL – Barnabys
BR – CJ Ott: B Coleman
57T – Dick Robinson: B Coleman
B – Tom McHugh: B Coleman
58,59 – Sven Gillsäter: Tiofoto
60 – roebild
63 – Russ Kinne: B Coleman
64 – Wilford L Miller
65 – TW Hall: WWF
66 – G Kinns
67 – James Simon: B Coleman
68,69 – Eric Hosking
70T – CJ Ott: B Coleman
B – Jan Grahn
73 – Eric Hosking
75 – Joe Van Wormer: B Coleman
76 – Okapia
77TL – Eric Hosking
CL – Joe Van Wormer
R – KB Newman
B – CJ Ott: B Coleman
78,79TL – Andre Fatras
C – Bavaria
TR – MP Price
B – KB Newman
80 – Okapia
83 – Rudolf Hofer
84 – Joe Van Wormer: B Coleman
86 – Okapia
87 – Eric Hosking
88T – Eric Hosking
B – W Puchalski: B Coleman
89 – Arthur Christiansen
90 – Eric Hosking
91 – Rudolf Hofer
95 – Russ Kinne: B Coleman
97T – John Warham

97B – Peter Johnson: NHPA
98T – John Markham
B – G Rüppell
99 – Bel G Vienne: Jacana
100T – H Schrempp
B – CJ Ott: B Coleman
101T – Carleton Ray: B Coleman
B – P Morrison: New Zealand Department of Internal Affairs, Wildlife Branch
102 – James Carr
103 – Frank Lane
104, 105, 107 – Eric Hosking
109 – Barnabys
110 – H Schrempp
111 – James Hancock: B Coleman
113T – H Schrempp
B – Eric Hosking
115 – Arthur Brook
117 – MF Soper
118T – Noel Simon
B – Eric Hosking
119 – Eric Hosking
120 – SC Porter: B Coleman
122 – Eric Hosking
125 – PH Ward
127TL,BR – W Zepf: NHPA
TR,BL – PH Ward
132 – Harold Oldroyd
133T – KH Hyatt
B – WS Bristowe
134L – Heather Angel
R – GE Hyde
135 – GE Hyde
136 – Anthony Bannister: NHPA
137 – Peter J Green
138 – PH Ward
139 – Swiss National Tourist Office
140 – Detleg Hecker: Bavaria
141 – Aerofilms
142 – Werner Bishoff: Magnum
143 – Popperfoto
144 – Swiss National Tourist Office
145 – Culver Pictures Inc
146 – Mount Everest Foundation
147 – CM Dixon